FRIENDS

OF

W9-DGE-385

Famous Fossil Finds

GREAT DISCOVERIES IN PALAEONTOLOGY

Fossilized bird

Famous Fossil Finds

GREAT DISCOVERIES IN PALAEONTOLOGY

By Raymond Holden

Illustrated by John Martinez

DODD, MEAD & COMPANY • NEW YORK

Copyright © 1966 by Raymond P. Holden
All rights reserved
No part of this book may be reproduced in any form
without permission in writing from the publisher
Library of Congress Catalog Card Number: 66-20448
Printed in the United States of America

CO. SCHOOLS
C645864

Acknowledgments

AMONG THE MANY who have helped in the preparation of this book I should mention first of all my wife, Barbara B. Holden.

Mrs. Joe Ann Daly of Dodd, Mead & Company contrived to make the usually tedious matter of guiding a book from manuscript to print a pleasant and stimulating experience.

For help in locating research material I am indebted to my sister-in-law, Miriam Young Holden. For special kindness and assistance I must thank Emil W. Allen, Jr., New Hampshire State Librarian. The Widener Library of Harvard University was particularly courteous and helpful. Without the resources of the Baker Library of Dartmouth College I could not have assembled much of the matter contained in this book.

I am especially grateful to Dr. Junius Bird of the Department of Archaeology, American Museum of Natural History, for the loan of material and photographs from his files.

Dr. Andrew H. McNair of the Department of Geology, Dartmouth College, generously provided me with an oral account of his recent discoveries in Victoria Island and a memorable view of the pre-Cambrian fossils which he brought back with him.

RAYMOND HOLDEN

Contents

Famous Fossil Finds
GREAT DISCOVERIES IN PALAEONTOLOGY

1.

Introduction

THE ELOQUENCE OF FOSSILS

IT IS ONLY WITHIN the past few thousand years that man has been able to keep written accounts of what he has thought, said and done. These few thousand years make up the era of what we know as history. Yet there are records much older than the records which man has written on clay tablets, papyrus, or scrolls, or set down in books. The earth has, you might almost say, known how to write for at least 500 million years. During that length of time it has kept careful records not only of the ancestors of man but of strange creatures and plants which did not survive until man appeared and would have been unknown to us but for the very special nature of the crust of the earth. Indeed, it is only during the last 150 years that we have developed our knowledge of them. One hundred and fifty years is a very short time in which to decipher the records of more than half a billion years.

Moreover, for very good reasons, the earth's record, which we have learned to read with surprising accuracy, is a very imperfect record. In order to be preserved and printed on the sheets or layers of the earth's crust, a living thing must in some way be protected from the fate of most living things after death—immediate decay and disintegration. Furthermore, the rare organism (*organism* is simply another way of saying *living thing*) which does escape the rapid ravage of decay must be covered by some shielding material in order to prevent the breakage and wearing away which could be caused by wind, water, ice, and great changes in temperature. It is obvious that only living things which have some relatively indestructible parts, such as skeletons or outer shells, have any chance of meeting the conditions which are required for entry in the book of earth.

Although the earth has undoubtedly existed for at least four and a half billion years—possibly as many as six billion—and life has probably existed on its surface for a large portion of that time, animals and plants did not develop parts which had any chance of being preserved between three billion and 600 million years ago. Fossil algae and primitive forms of plant life have recently been found on the northern shore of Lake Superior in rocks which are known to be at least 1,900,000,000 years old. Minute particles which some scientists believe to be remains of living organisms, though others do not, have been found in African rocks at least three billion years old. Yet there is a gap between the date of these early forms of plant life and the date of the earliest known fossil forms of animal life, forms which are too complex to have been evolved in less than many millions of years.

Even during the later periods of the earth's development from a landless planet into the home of man, the chance of a dead animal or plant meeting all the conditions necessary for survival as what we call a fossil was very slight. Our knowledge of the enormous number of animals and plants which have become extinct is ex-

Petrified wood, a fossil fern, and dinosaur tracks

tremely limited. Great and thrilling as the discoveries of the last 150 years have been, they have brought us certain knowledge of only a very small percentage of the total number of forms of life which once existed on earth. Most of them we shall never know.

The word "fossil" is an interesting one and there are probably few people of grade school age or over who have not at least a general idea of what it means. It comes, of course, from the Latin word *fossilis* (from *fodere*, "to dig") meaning "dug up." This suggests, rather than that fossils have to be dug up, merely that they were once buried, or in some way covered. The word, however, does not convey a true sense of the variety of things which are considered as fossils.

First, there are once-living things which, because of special con-

3

ditions which prevailed at the time of their death in the place where they died, have been preserved more or less as they were. Insects have been preserved in the gum of pine trees (called amber) for many thousands of years. Mammoths, as we shall see, have been preserved in ice. Bones and shells have been kept as they once were in tar and oil. Then, and these are far more common, there are bones and shells, tree trunks, and other porous parts of living things in which the original matter—nerves, and channels for arteries and veins—has been replaced by minerals and has, as we say, become petrified, or "turned to stone."

There are, too, molds and casts of organisms which, after being covered with sand or soil, have completely dissolved but left cavities, shaped as the organisms were, into which mineral matter has flowed and hardened. Another form of preservation is the retention, in what once was soft material but which has become hardened, of footprints, snail tracks, and the like. Before being washed away by rain, running water, or tide, these were covered by a layer of protective material which eventually, under the pressure of what the ages heaped upon it, became hardened. An excellent example of this form of fossil preservation are the many dinosaur footprints in the Connecticut River valley between Holyoke and South Hadley, Massachusetts.

A form of fossil which may seem both improbable and useless, but which has been of great value to scientists, is the coprolite, or "dung-stone" (from two Greek words meaning *dung* and *stone*), which is exactly what it sounds like—the fossilized dung of animals. This is often found in association with animal skeletons and gives, through minute examination, clues to the types of plants which grew at the time the animal flourished and which formed a part of his diet. The importance of this form of fossil will be seen in Chapter 10.

We speak, rather scornfully, of someone who is aged and shows little active sense of life as an "old fossil," as if fossils were dead things. In spirit they are far from dead, for they are the seeds of a knowledge to which our life today owes much. In them, in spite of the gaps in the record, is the story of the orderly march of the life force through change after change from the simple primitive cell to man.

If all the varieties of fossils unearthed by man had been found in a single layer near the surface of the earth, it would have been impossible for scientists to have divided the past, as they have done, into periods of time. The surface, or crust, of the earth is, at least in the parts which are not covered with water, something like 20 miles thick. (About 29 per cent, or a little more than a quarter of the total surface, is land.) Most of the material of which the land is composed was undoubtedly thrown out from lower down by volcanoes which formed in weak spots in the upper layers of earth and provided an escape for the burned rock and ash consumed by the heat resulting from the pressure of shrinking. In the millions, perhaps billions, of years since the earth's crust as we know it was

Fossils: insect imbedded in amber, impression of a bird, a trilobite

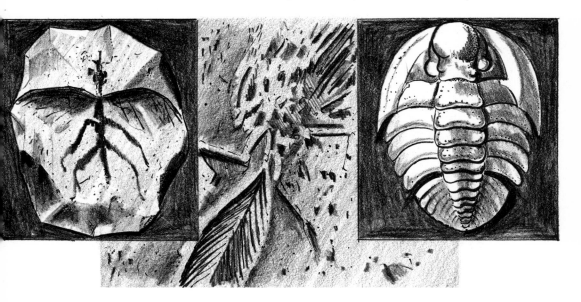

formed, there have been many alternate risings and fallings of the rocks and much covering up of ancient layers by substances washed down from mountains. The crust of the earth, however, is not like an onion with layer after layer of deposited silt and stone. There have been enormous upheavals which have broken and distorted the layers so that in some places, such as the area about the junction of the states of Colorado, Wyoming, and Utah, the rocks laid down 70 million years ago are at the surface and the skeletons of creatures which then lived but have few or no relatives alive on earth today are exposed. This condition accounts for the story told in Chapter 8.

This is not a history of man's efforts to read the book of the past—efforts which, with the study involved in them, make up the science of palaeontology. Palaeontology is a large word derived from several Greek words which roughly mean "knowledge of things which existed long ago." There is another word, archaeology, also from the Greek and also meaning, roughly, knowledge of things which existed long ago. Archaeology really means knowledge of things from the beginning, which would seem to make it more suitable as a name for study of the most ancient past than palaeontology, which merely means very old. Be that as it may, it has been decided that the word archaeology will be limited to traces of ancient man, and that palaeontology will be used for the science which deals with ancient living things which existed before man was known on earth.

As man's knowledge of his own past and of the past of his fellow creatures has expanded—man's past being pushed back and the past of his fellow creatures being pulled forward—the two have come to overlap considerably. An example of this overlapping, wherein it is hard to make a distinction between palaeontology and archaeology, is given in Chapter 9.

The stories in this book are not told with any idea that they will give the reader a complete picture of the world of the past. The intention is to present a series of accounts which will give a few highlights of man's struggle to unravel the very complicated story of the development of life from its earliest beginnings. It is the author's hope that these stories, some of them not very widely known, will lead those who read them to go on to further reading, to more complete study, perhaps even to considering palaeontology as a career. Certainly the story of the many often amazing forms of life which have existed, endured, or ceased to exist on earth, will never be completely told. It will never cease to be interesting.

2.

How a Little Girl Became a Celebrity
THE FISH-LIZARD OF LYME REGIS

IN THE SOUTHWESTERN PART of Dorsetshire, England, where chalk and sand and rock face the restless waters of the Channel, lies a quaint old town which would be known simply as Lyme had not a part of it been surrendered to the Crown in the fourteenth century. Since 1316, which seems a long time ago, and according to British custom which allows a town associated with a monarch to add a Latin word meaning "of the King," the town has been known as Lyme Regis. Yet the fame of Lyme Regis is based upon something far older than King Edward III.

On either side of the valley worn into the high land by ancient waters, great cliffs face the sea. At the foot is the village of Lyme Regis. The rocks of which these cliffs are composed are very ancient indeed. The series to which they belong was formed, perhaps a hundred million years ago, in what must have been a shallow sea. It was a sea inhabited by creatures quite unknown in the days when Lyme became a borough of the Crown. Not until the great mind of Leonardo da Vinci dominated the last part of the fifteenth and the first part of the sixteenth century was there any recognition of the fact that what we call fossils were the remains of animals and plants caught in the fissures and layers of the earth's ever-changing crust. Not for another two and a half centuries, when James Hutton published his *Theory of the Earth* in 1785, did the true meaning of the heaped and tilted layers of rock which men had known, used, and misinterpreted for centuries begin to become clear.

In Lyme Regis at the time when Hutton's world-shaking book was published lived a carpenter named Richard Anning. He was not prosperous and had plenty of time to wander about the shore and its cliffs of layered and crumbling rock. Here he was in the habit of picking up shells and the stony images of creatures caught in the sediments of an ancient sea and raised by the pressures of

Ammonites and belemnites

earth's crust to rest above the beaches of Dorsetshire. One of the commonest of these creatures was a mollusk, which the natives of Lyme Regis knew as a "cornemonius," a corruption of *cornu ammonis*, or "horn of Ammon." Today we would call this large, flattened spiral shell an ammonite. Although there are no living specimens anywhere, ammonites were quite popular with travelers along the post road north of Lyme and the "cury men," or curio dealers, of whom Richard Anning was one, carried them in baskets to the post stations on the highway and sold them to coach passengers while the horses were being changed.

Richard Anning was not an orthodox churchman. He was a dissenter and he liked to show his dissent by choosing church holy days, when the church people were at prayer, to do his collecting. He was sometimes helped in his curio-gathering by his only daughter, Mary, who was born in 1799. Richard gathered ammonites, belemnites (which are extinct relatives of the modern squid), and the fossil vertebrae of ancient reptiles, known to the "cury men" as "verterberries." These last were common in the rocks of Lyme Regis.

What Richard Anning thought of his "cornemoniuses" and "verterberries" is not recorded, but we do know that at the beginning of the nineteenth century superstition was more popular than textbooks. When a blight appeared on the leaves of the seaside blackberries it was attributed to a blackening of the air by some mysterious flying serpent. People in Lyme Regis firmly believed that the scourge would cause the death of nineteen out of twenty persons under thirty years of age. Be that as it may, Mary Anning survived, though her father died when she was in her eleventh year. She lived, but she had a narrow escape.

When the child was fifteen months old, she was put in charge of a nurse, Mrs. Haskins. Mrs. Haskins did not, it seems, believe in giving up her personal pleasure in order to do justice to the duties of a baby-sitter. With little Mary in her arms and two female companions she journeyed one afternoon to what was known as the "Rack Field," outside of Lyme, to see what must have been a kind of circus performance. The afternoon was hot and sultry. At about five o'clock a violent thunderstorm blanketed the field with torrents of rain and jagged arrows of lightning. The spectators rushed for shelter—some toward home, some toward the sheds and outhouses which surrounded the field.

Mrs. Haskins and her friends decided very unwisely that a great elm below the field would provide shelter enough. The elm was struck by lightning and Mrs. Haskins and her two companions were killed instantly. Those who came, as the rain let up, to see what had happened found Mary lying on the ground with the others, apparently lifeless. Her rescuers soaked the baby in warm water, however, and she not only revived but became, and remained, a lively and intelligent child, although up to that time she had been described as a dull and sickly baby.

It is very unlikely that Mary's father could have known much about the fossils which he collected. Very few men, indeed, knew at the time of Richard Anning's death what a fossil was, much less that an ammonite was part of the chain of life in which man himself was a link. Anning had been able only to teach his daughter where to look for the curious objects. But Mary kept on collecting, perhaps because she liked being on the beaches and cliffs of Lyme Regis. It is said that one day, after her father's death, when she was coming home from the beach with a good ammonite in her basket she met a lady who offered her half a crown for the specimen, which looked a little like a grayish stone Danish pastry. The child went home with the half crown in her pocket, determined, if it was that easy, to make a business of collecting and so help support herself and her mother.

Mary had had little schooling and she apparently got none at all after her father died. She was a sturdy, serious little girl with a round face and very bright dark eyes which were extremely keen. She had a natural intelligence, a boundless curiosity, and an interest which did not let her curiosity be satisfied with merely finding things.

In 1810, the year that Richard Anning died, scientists were beginning to remember what Leonardo da Vinci had suggested three hundred years earlier, and what the world had since forgotten—that fossils were undoubtedly the remains of plants and animals and perhaps might be used to explain the world's history. Some of the learned men who were interested began coming to Lyme Regis to have a look at the treasury of the past which seemed to be located in its rocks. When they did they usually took on young Mary Anning as a guide. Her conversation with these scientists soon made her realize that what her father had regarded as mere curios to be traded for shillings and pence were far more than that. She somehow found the means of understanding that many of the objects which she unearthed were in fact parts which could be fitted together to make a skeleton, even though it might be the skeleton of something unknown.

A scientist named Karl Koenig was Keeper of the Department of Natural History at the British Museum. Koenig had concluded, from a study of fragments sent to him, that there must once have existed in the seas of the Jurassic Epoch (the sediments of one of which had formed the rocks about Lyme Regis) a strange creature resembling a fish and yet more like a reptile. No such fish-lizard had ever been found, but Koenig was convinced that it had once lived. He had a fairly good idea of what it should look like.

Mary Anning undoubtedly knew nothing of Dr. Koenig's no-

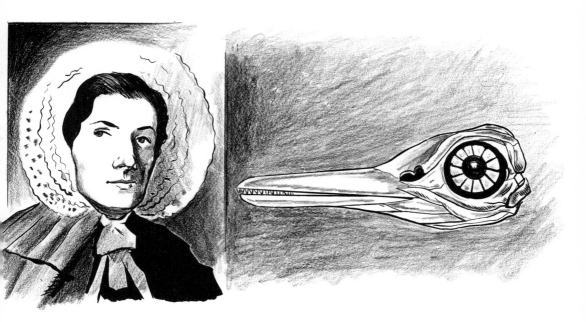

Mary Anning
in later life

Skull of Ichthyosaurus

tion of the fish-lizard, which he had, even before it was proved to exist, named *Ichthyosaurus*, from two Greek words, the first meaning fish and the second, reptile or lizard. Yet she was constantly turning stones and examining everything, eager to find something she had never seen before. At about the time of her father's death her brother had found a strange fishlike head, long, narrow, and heavily toothed. Neither he nor Mary had any idea what the head belonged to and no visiting scientist happened along to make any suggestion.

One day in 1811 Mary, roaming the rocks to the eastward of Lyme with her hammer and her little black and white dog Tray, saw something unusual, something dull white and streaky protruding from the gray-blue rock at the base of the cliff. She seems to have known, although there was nothing but instinct to tell her, not what it was, but certainly that it was immensely important. She knew enough not to whack at it with her hammer, seeing that it was too large and too deeply embedded for her to handle. There she stood in her heavy wool clothes, her skirts pinned up, her sturdy legs braced upon the wooden pattens (heavy leather shoes with wooden soles) which she wore to protect her feet from the ooze and slip of the tide. She stared at the strange stone bones, shadowed by the dark cliffs overhead, listening to the surge and wash of the gentle waves of the bay which seemed to say, "Time! Shhh! Time! Shhh!"

Something within her told her what to do. She hurried across the wet beach and over the stone and timber pier called the Cobb and found some friendly men who were willing to come and help her. Under her supervision they carefully freed a slab of the crumbling rock, once the bottom of a long lost sea, which contained, intact, the skeleton of an unknown sea creature. How Mary had come by the skill, which she already possessed, and which enabled her to chip and brush away the enclosing stone leaving the skeleton unharmed, no one will ever know. Neither can we know whether she saw at once that here was the body to which belonged the curious head found by her brother. This girl of twelve had found—and she was the first human being to do so—the nearly complete skeleton of Karl Koenig's *Ichthyosaurus*.

Lyme Regis now became a magic word to those scientists, palaeontologists, who were interested in ancient life on earth. They came to see the extraordinary cliffs and to talk to Mary Anning. Many a scholar was guided over the beaches and slipping layers of rock by the little girl who had, by her keenness of eye and her quick intelligence, enabled the science of ancient life to take such a tremendous step forward. Mary became acquainted with the

14

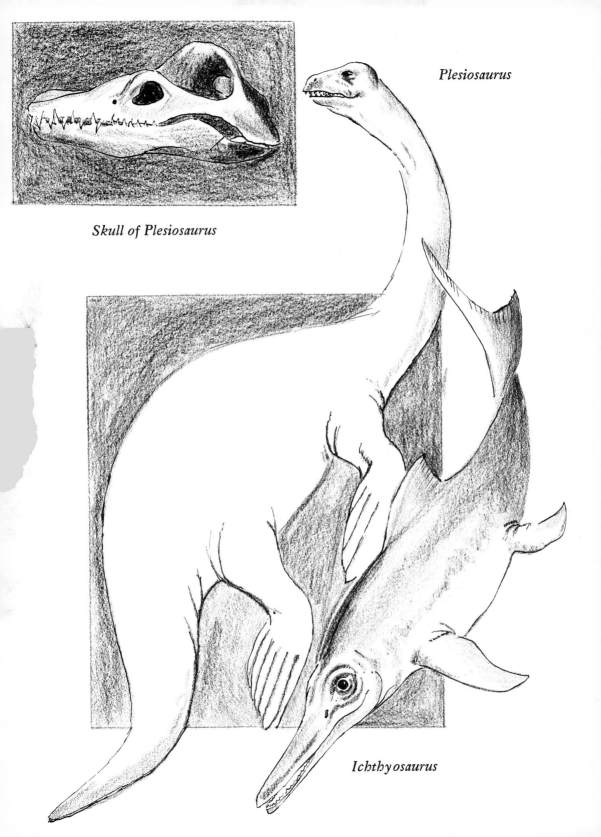

Skull of Plesiosaurus

Plesiosaurus

Ichthyosaurus

best of them and in spite of her lack of education she learned much from them and applied what she learned to her trade.

One of those who came to see her, William D. Conybere, told her of a creature which he had described from fragments, as Koenig had described the *Ichthyosaurus*. In 1824, now a young woman of twenty-five, Mary located an almost complete skeleton of Conybere's *Plesiosaurus*. This was a creature nearly eight feet long which had once been a land-dwelling reptile but which had adapted itself to life in the sea rather than perish when the waters took over the region in which it lived.

Mary Anning got enough (it was said to be £150) for this remarkable find to finance still further searches. Her increasing skill and developing knowledge enabled her to recognize more and more objects of value. She located several ichthyosaurs after the first one and was able to notice differences among them which were of great importance. In association with one which she described in a letter with appreciative care, she found coprolites (fossil waste matter from the body) which showed plainly what the *Ichthyosaurus* had been eating. The stony lumps found near the base of the tail contained the remains of squid.

In 1828, when Mary was still less than thirty years old, she made her third great discovery, the complete remains of a described but until then unlocated creature called a *Dimorphodon*, a kind of Pterodactyl (which means "wing-finger"). This fantastic creature was a flying reptile, with an elongated turtle-like head, a mouth full of large and small teeth, membrane-like wings stretched from the elongated fourth finger of what would be its hands to its hind legs, and a long tail like that of an enormous rat. The skeleton of Mary Anning's *Dimorphodon* is on exhibition today in the Fossil Reptile Gallery of the British Museum, together with her *Plesiosaurus* and a portrait of the remarkable Mary herself.

During her lifetime Mary only got to London once. There, she ceased to be the eager fossil-hunter and became the young small-town girl, reverently impressed by the number and beauty of the churches, overawed by a sight of the first Queen Elizabeth's handwriting and the jewels in the Tower of London. Back in Lyme Regis, however, she was not at all in awe of the great folk who came to see her. She enjoyed displaying her knowledge to scientists and took considerable pleasure in leading them into fields of talk in which she knew more than they did.

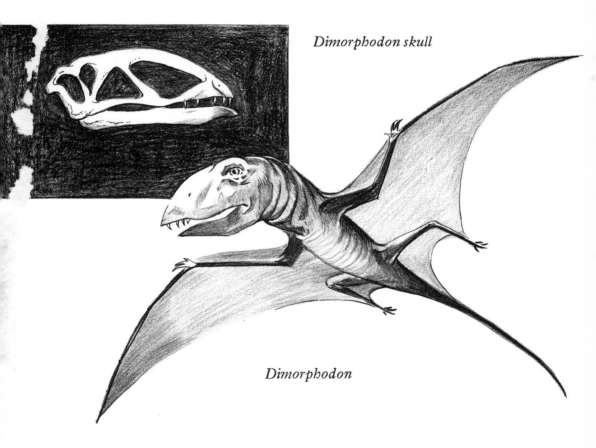

Dimorphodon skull

Dimorphodon

When King Frederick of Saxony visited Lyme Regis and bought a small fossil *Ichthyosaurus* from Mary, he asked her to write her name in his notebook. This she did, but could not resist suggesting to him that it really was not necessary as the King would find that she was very well known in Europe.

Mary never married, although she apparently was very much in love at one time. She died of cancer in her forty-eighth year. In the little church at Lyme Regis there is a stained glass window commemorating her services to science.

3.

When Is a Fossil Not a Fossil?
THE COELACANTH'S STORY

IN THE ROCKS of Dorset in England, where Mary Anning had such success in locating the bones of creatures whose existence had been predicted, but not verified, a peculiar kind of fossil fish had occasionally been found. It was not a very large fish; most specimens were not more than 20 inches long. These creatures, which scientists agreed had become extinct at about the time the dinosaurs disappeared, belonged to a group which developed fins that were so much like legs that their possessors could crawl out of the water with them. This skill was very useful to the fish, which were called fringe-fins, or *crossopterygians* (which is pronounced just the way it is spelled).

The fringe-fins, so-called because they had at the ends of their stumpy, footlike fins a fringe of hollow spines, lived on land for a long time, some of them developing into amphibians (the ancestors of frogs and newts), which, although they lived most of their lives on land breathing air, could go into the water when they wished. Their fins really became legs. One group of the crossopterygians, for some reason, did not remain on land. They returned to the sea and became fish again, although they kept some traces of their sojourn on land. Their legs became fins again although they were built like legs. These fishes became known as *coelacanths* (pronounced "sealacanth"), which means "hollow spines," from the peculiar bristle-like ends of their fins and tails. The coelacanths were quite successful fishes. They spread over a great part of all the oceans.

We know of them through their fossil skeletons which have been found in rocks formed 70 or more million years ago. No traces of them have ever been found in rocks less than 70 million years old. This being the case, scientists felt that they were justified in believing that the coelacanths had ceased to exist 70 million years ago. No one doubted that they were extinct. They had been accurately described from their fossil skeletons and any scientist would have recognized a live one had he seen it. Until 1938, that was how the coelacanth stood in the world of fishes, ancient and modern—an extinct creature of the past.

On December 22, 1938, a fishing boat working out of East London, South Africa, some 600 miles east of Cape Town, was on its way back to port with a disappointing catch. The captain decided to have one more try before going in. He threw out his nets in a very unlikely place where the sea was relatively shallow, barely 250 feet deep, and full of sharp rocks jutting up from the bottom. The haul, however, was a good one—some three and a half tons—although more than half of it was sharks which could be used only for fertilizer.

While sorting out the fish on deck as the trawler headed for port the crew came upon a single fish, some five feet long and very lively, which none of them had ever seen before. The captain left the wheel to have a look at it and poke it with a stick. The strange monster writhed and slapped and tried to crush the stick with its heavily-toothed jaws.

December is hot in that part of South Africa. Although the great fish lived much longer than the food fish and the sharks, the blazing sun was finally too much for it and it died. Fortunately the captain did not throw it overboard. He remembered an agreement which his company had made with the East London museum —an agreement to let the curator of the museum know whenever a trawler came into port with its catch.

The curator of the museum was a young woman, Miss M. C. Courtenay-Latimer, who was extremely interested in fish. Miss Latimer hurried down to the port when she heard that there was something on board the trawler which the captain thought she ought to see. When the men pointed it out to her she gave a cry of astonishment. The creature lay there exuding an unusually vile smell. Its jaws were strong and fierce, even in death. Its body was covered with thick bluish scales and its tail was large and fleshy with a finlike fringe of spines and a small secondary tail like a paint

A prehistoric amphibian

brush sticking out of the center of the main tail. The heavy fins were more like the flippers of a seal than ordinary fish fins. Miss Latimer did not know how remarkable it would prove to be, but, in any case, it would be quite a prize for the little East London museum. The prize, however, smelled worse every minute and it weighed 127 pounds.

Somehow Miss Latimer and her native assistant got the unappetizing burden to the museum. She knew that in the hot December weather the unknown specimen would not last long enough to be identified. She managed to persuade a reluctant director of the museum, who was not much interested in dead, uneatable fish, to allow her money to have the creature mounted by a taxidermist—a man who makes his living preserving birds, beasts, and fishes by skinning and stuffing them. The museum directors, however, would give her nothing with which to pay for a study of her fish. Miss Latimer went through all the books she had but found nothing even remotely resembling it. She knew that she must get help somewhere.

The young museum curator remembered that she had heard of a professor at the university at Grahamstown, some 100 miles from East London, who made a specialty of fishes. He was the leading authority on African fishes. The day after Miss Latimer had obtained her unknown fish she wrote to Dr. J. L. B. Smith, telling him about the discovery and describing the weird creature. Could the professor please tell her what it was?

Dr. Smith, unfortunately, was spending the Christmas holidays outside a little village in the back country. He did not receive Miss Latimer's letter until January 3, by which time the taxidermist who was mounting the fish had found it necessary to throw away most of the soft parts. Dr. Smith realized, as he read the letter from East London, what Miss Latimer's fish might be, but he found it very difficult to let himself believe in it. He at first thought that someone had made a mistake. He tried to telephone Miss Latimer but could not reach her. He had to be content with a telegram telling her to be sure to preserve the skeleton and the gills. But even if the great fish had had a real fish skeleton, which it did not, it was too late.

Smith was in a frenzy of excitement. He wrote a letter to Miss Latimer telling her of his interest. He said that what she had described resembled an extinct fish but that he couldn't be sure until he had a look at it. The next morning he found that his excitement had grown instead of being replaced by sober thought. He made another attempt, this time successful, to reach the East London museum by phone. He was desperately unhappy when he learned that everything found inside the fish's skin had been thrown into the sea. He decided to go to East London in any case and study what was left of the mysterious creature. Dr. Smith, however, had things to do before he could leave for the coast. In the meantime, while he corrected examination papers, he wired to Cape Town for a copy of the catalogue of fossil fishes of the British Museum. When the book came and he had time to study it he felt that there was no doubt about Miss Latimer's find. It was a fossil fish—the coelacanth, which had been missing for 70 million years. In spite of the all but positive identification, there were problems. In the first place, if there was one living specimen, there must be others. Why had they not been found before? In the second place, why was the fish so large? The coelacanths of 70 million years ago had been less than two feet in length. Miss Latimer's specimen was five feet long.

At last, more than two weeks after the capture of the ancient fish, Dr. Smith arrived in East London and hurried to the museum. The creature, even without the frame of cartilage which served it as a skeleton, even without its heart and brain which would have told much about its history, seemed even more remarkable than Dr. Smith had imagined it.

The scientist realized that he must first describe the fish for some scientific journal, giving it a scientific name, something which the one first to describe a discovery is privileged to do. Dr. Smith called the coelacanth *Latimeria chalumnae* Smith, for it was Miss Latimer who had first brought his attention to the specimen, it had been caught near the mouth of the Chalumna River, and he, Smith, was the first to describe it. Even after christening the creature and introducing it to science, it would be necessary to find another specimen so that it might be studied in detail. After considering the problem of the apparently sudden discovery of an extinct creature, Smith concluded that the live coelacanth, *Latimeria*, must live somewhere in the area bounded by East Africa on the west, the great island of Madagascar on the east, the Comoro Islands on the north, and East London on the south. He made inquiries and offered rewards.

Then came World War II. Dr. Smith had to turn to other things. *Latimeria* was not forgotten but had to be neglected. In 1945, when the war was over, the professor was asked to write a book about South African fishes, which was just what he wanted to do. This turned his attention once more to the coelacanth. He did not have the means to organize an expedition to search for new specimens. He had to be satisfied with having a leaflet printed which carried a picture and description of the fish and offered a reward of £100 to anyone who could get one for him.

Nothing happened for a long time. Dr. Smith's book on South African fishes was published and, to his surprise, became a success. The professor and his wife were able to travel about and make inquiries. They found one man who said he had once

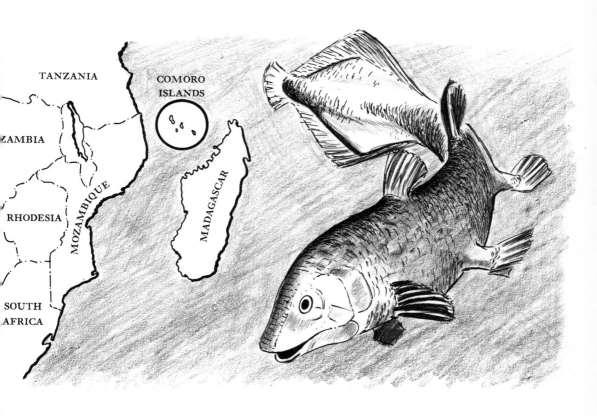

Coelacanth

caught a fish like the description of the coelacanth but he could not remember where. They met another man who ran a trading vessel between Africa and the Comoro Islands who expressed interest and promised to keep his eyes open.

In 1952, when Dr. Smith and his wife were returning to Grahamstown from their travels, they docked at Durban. While in port, one of the ship's officers handed the professor a telegram. It was from Eric Hunt, the trader, who was in the Comoro Islands at a place called Dzaondzi on the island of Pamanzi. The cable had been forwarded from Grahamstown and was four days old when Dr. Smith received it. It said that Hunt had a five-foot

25

coelacanth into which he had injected as much formalin, a preservative, as he could locate. He wanted to know what to do next. The dead fish, like the telegram, was four days old. And the fish was 2,000 miles away.

Dr. Smith had to think fast. His ship was to leave Durban on the following day and he would have to go with it if he had no other plan. After many difficulties the professor got through to South African Prime Minister Malan, who had seen Smith's book on South African fishes and realized the importance of the coelacanth. Dr. Malan ordered a military plane to be sent for the professor to carry him to the Comoro Islands—if possible. No one seemed to be sure that the islands possessed a landing field for aircraft. It was the cyclone season and over the sea, between Mozambique and the Comores, the clouds were thick and ominously colored. Nevertheless the plane passed over the island of Mayotte, the largest of the Comores. There was no airfield there. On to the smaller island of Pamanzi. Here the pilot located a tiny landing strip. They landed and found Hunt there to meet them. The great fish, he said, was safe on his boat, where it was beyond the reach of the government authorities who might want to claim it for France since it had been caught in French waters.

Smith insisted on going to see it before he attended a reception which the local authorities had arranged for him. When he saw it, he knew it was a coelacanth but as it was somewhat different from the first specimen, having no forward dorsal fin and no little extra paint-brush tail, he thought it was a different species. It turned out not to be. After a reception at the French Governor's house, while the fish was loaded on the South African plane, Smith, the pilot, and his crew boarded the plane and, anxious to get away before the French changed their minds about letting him have the fish for which he had paid the £100 reward, and even more anxious to get out of the cyclone belt, they took off and were soon in the chill air high above the sultry clouds. The fish and its smell rode with them. Although the creature was fairly well preserved with formalin and was complete, inside and out, it was not a pleasant companion. Dr. Smith, nevertheless, was happy. He had his specimen to dissect and describe. The coelacanth was no longer a fossil.

Since 1952 at least a dozen more *Latimeria* have been taken. It has become apparent that, ancient and primitive as they are, they have not been truly missing for 70 million years. In fact, the native fishermen of the Comoro Islands have been catching them for as long as they can remember. They even had a name for the living fossil. They called it *kombessa*. Had it not been for Miss Courtenay-Latimer and her unusual interest, no one can say how long it might have been before *kombessa* and *Latimeria chalumnae* Smith became one. Scientists who have studied it have not yet been able to explain how the great fish managed to survive, almost unchanged and completely unknown, for many more years than man has lived on earth.

4.

The Eggs Which Time Cooked
ROY CHAPMAN ANDREWS' DINOSAURS

GREAT DISCOVERIES have been made in all fields of science as a result of sound thinking on the part of great men. Great finds have also been made as a result of some fortunate accident. There is still a third way of discovering important things. This consists in finding something while you are looking for something else. Columbus re-discovered America (the Norsemen had apparently already found and forgotten a different part of it) while he was looking for the Far East.

A great American scientist, Henry Fairfield Osborn, had, at the beginning of the twentieth century, been thinking much about the beginnings of the human race. Osborn was thoroughly familiar with all the forms of life which had been discovered in fossil form. He believed, for reasons which are rather too complicated to go into here, that all of the life on land in Europe and America had grown and branched out from a source in Central Asia.

Professor Osborn had often spoken of this belief to a member of the staff of the American Museum of Natural History, of which Osborn was president. This staff member was Roy Chapman Andrews, who had joined the Museum after leaving college. He had collected for the Museum in Korea, Burma, and China, knew something of the Chinese language, and something of the nature of the land in Central Asia.

Andrews proposed to President Osborn that a great Central Asiatic Expedition be organized to study the living and fossil life of Central Asia and to search for traces of the origin of man. The Museum sponsored the expedition and many wealthy men contributed to the fund which made it possible. Noted scientists in many fields formed the staff. The transportation in Asia was to be a combination of camel and automobile caravan—the camels to transport gasoline, equipment, and supplies and the automobiles, which had never before been used for exploration in that part of the world, to carry the staff.

The expedition, which was to last five years, set out for China in 1921. The first year, during which things were complicated by civil war in China, was largely devoted to organizing headquarters and studying the problems to be faced. By the summer of 1922 Roy Andrews had his expedition in the field, camped in the very center of the Gobi Desert in what was known as Outer Mongolia, about midway between the Arctic Ocean and the Bay of Bengal and more than 700 miles west of Peking. Andrews and his men had made their way across the almost unknown desert, through gravel, sand, gullies, scattered rocks, dry water courses, and mile after mile of sandy hummocks covered with scrub growth. The cars were frequently stuck in loose sand up to their hubs and had to be pushed out. The expedition had only a Russian map, which showed a great range of mountains, 6,000 feet high, directly in the way of their route toward a well, hundreds of miles away, where they were to meet the camel caravan. Water was getting low, casks and bags were empty. If the mountains proved to be an obstacle which would be too much for the heavily loaded cars, the expedition would indeed be in danger. Andrews told his navigators to set a course directly for the well. In the meantime, the leader took a detour toward what looked like, and proved to be, a group of three Mongol tents. He left his photographer, J. B. Shackleford, to wait for the following cars. When the inhabitants of the tents had recovered from their fear of Andrews' motor car, they told him of a well not far away.

When the rest of the cars reached Shackleford, he told them to wait for Andrews to return while he himself took a walk toward the north, where he had noticed an unusual red cliff. The cliff turned out to be one edge of a great depression full of wind-worn pinnacles of sandstone. Resting on one of the pinnacles, where it had been exposed by the wearing down of the sandstone, was a gleaming white skull. Shackleford walked back to join the others and showed them the strange skull. Neither Walter Granger, the expedition's palaeontologist, nor Professor Berkey, the geologist, had ever seen one like it, although they knew it was a reptile.

When Andrews joined his men, it appeared that Shackleford's valley was the site of the well which the Mongol had recommended. The excited men moved in and camped. It was hard to wait until camp was made, for in a great bowl of salmon- and rose-colored rock which rain and frost, with the help of the fierce desert wind, had gouged out of the sandstone, were scattered towers and pinnacles and tiered castles of colored stone. Great crevices like baby canyons split the rock walls. In all the cliffs and

Roy Chapman Andrews

outcroppings of rock, white bones stood out against the red stone which, in the evening sunlight, seemed almost to be on fire. Andrews and his men knew that they had found a great burying ground of ancient life, but they knew, too, that the terrible Mongolian winter might be upon them at any minute, so late in the season was it. They had to get to their camel caravan before it was too late.

Fortunately, when the navigators took bearings on sun and stars they found that they had already crossed the mountains shown on the Russian map. The mountains simply did not exist. In the morning, with no time to dig up even a single skeleton, they set out. They reached the caravan before the blizzards struck and made their way back to Peking, carrying Shackleford's precious reptile skull. From Peking, the skull was sent back to New York for study. Weeks later a cable arrived from President Osborn announcing that the skull they had found was that of the missing ancestor of a group of huge horned dinosaurs called *ceratopsians* which had been found in North America but whose origin no one had understood. Dr. Osborn urged Andrews to return to the spot, which the expedition had named "The Flaming Cliffs," and search for more treasures of the distant past.

In the summer of 1923 Andrews did return to Mongolia to the expedition's camp site of the year before. Within a few hours after making camp each man in the group had found at least one dinosaur skeleton. The red valley seemed to be paved and walled with bones. All of the staff hoped that some of the skeletons might turn out to be human, thus giving support to Professor Osborn's theory of the Central Asiatic origin of life. They found no trace of human life that could not be referred to the present-day Mongolian inhabitants of the region. When the expedition had left the United States, the newspaper had played up the idea that it was on its way to Asia to look for the "Missing Link"—the evolutionary link between man and the lower animals. What Andrews and his staff found at The Flaming Cliffs gave the press a new headline which was played up to the limit, and incidentally helped to finance the remaining years of the expedition's work.

At noon, on the day after the expedition's arrival at The Flaming Cliffs, one of the staff palaeontologists, George Olsen, came into camp with a strange story. He said that in a ledge not far from camp he had found what he was sure were petrified eggs. His companions thought that he was either playing a practical joke on them or that he had found some sort of egg-shaped desert con-

Protoceratops

cretions (stones formed, as a pearl is formed in an oyster, around some small bit of usually organic matter among the layers of sedimentary rocks). Olsen insisted that he was serious and that what he had found were really eggs. His companions followed him to the spot where he had made his find. There lay Olsen's eggs—three of them, each about eight inches long.

Walter Granger, the expedition's chief palaeontologist, was convinced but puzzled. He knew that the rocks of The Flaming Cliffs dated from a period (known as Cretaceous, from the Latin word for "chalk") during which he was sure that there had been

Dinosaur eggs

no birds large enough to lay such eggs. What was more, these eggs were not shaped like the birds' eggs we know. They were longer and somewhat flatter. Nevertheless they were certainly eggs. The shell, which was quite thick, seemed to have little pores in it which definitely suggested those in the shell of a large bird's egg. The only thing Granger could think of, since after all The Flaming Cliffs were a dinosaur burying ground, was that the strange objects were dinosaur eggs. Yet no one had ever seen or heard of a dinosaur egg. Since dinosaurs were reptiles, it had been assumed that they did produce eggs, but whether the eggs were hatched inside or outside the body no one knew. No one really expected to find out.

The excited men began looking about for more eggs. They found many, some whole, some cracked, and some mere fragments of shell. Approximately four inches above the level in which the eggs were found, Olsen discovered the skeleton of a small, toothless dinosaur, about four feet long, which undoubtedly had been preying upon the eggs of his relatives and, while at it, had been buried too deeply for escape in the drift of some desert sandstorm. The accumulation of this storm was in its turn covered by other storms and not again exposed for some eighty million years.

If any member of the expedition had doubts about the nature of these eggs, the discovery of several which contained the tiny skeletons of unborn dinosaurs must have resolved them. The Central Asiatic Expedition had given something new to science. When the news broke, the world could apparently think of nothing else. The discovery of the eggs made people who had accepted the idea of the great dinosaurs of the past but still regarded them as something mythical, like the medieval dragon, regard them as creatures which they could understand, no more mythical than man himself.

5.

CO. SCHOOLS

C645864

Enter Feathers

ARCHAEOPTERYX, THE FIRST TRUE BIRD

IT IS EASIER for the palaeontologist to say that birds are descended from reptiles than it is for the average person, who knows little about the development of animal life, to believe it. For a long time it was impossible for even the palaeontologist to prove it. Yet today the reptilian ancestry of birds is an accepted fact, even though the point in time at which bird and reptile parted company must have been from 150 to 190 million years ago.

The reptiles of that distant age had begun to be at home on land and had tried a number of experiments calculated to make them at home in the air as well. Those experiments, of which there is a fossil record—we can call them experiments although they may have gone on for ten million years—were not permanently successful. The Pterodactyls, literally, "wing-fingers" (see Chapter 1) seem to have had upon their bodies neither scales, feathers, nor hair, but attempted the conquest of the air by means of a membrane-like skin stretched from an enormous fourth finger to the

35

leg. The earliest Pterodactyls, which did not quite succeed in conquering the air, nevertheless lived long enough to develop a gigantic variety with a 22-foot wingspread. This great creature could do little more than glide like a sailplane, presumably over the sea, since he probably could not have taken off from the land and could not carry fuel enough to develop the energy necessary for flights inland which would have to end, as they began, in the sea. The sea, unless he could find a large body of water inland, would have been the only place in which he could get a long enough run to take off.

The Pterodactyls were entirely reptiles, though of a novel form and, because they lived in and over the sea, many of them have been preserved, like that found by Mary Anning. Creatures dying in the sea have a better chance than land animals of being covered, before decaying, by the constant rain and drift of sediments on the sea bottom. Until the middle of the nineteenth century we knew nothing about those reptile-like yet unreptilian successors of the Pterodactyls who, on land, developed a better system of flying and became what we know as birds.

The matter of speaking of some animal that lived as much as 50 or 100 million years ago as the ancestor of a creature now living, especially when the so-called ancestor is an entirely different sort of being, is very confusing to most of us. This is partly because, even a hundred years after Darwin, the idea of evolution of animal form, although generally accepted, is very incompletely understood by most people. That is because one can hardly conceive of the enormous periods of time which are required to produce bodily changes. It is easy to understand that a creature who is successful in meeting the conditions of his time is likely to survive and one whose bodily form keeps him from being successful is not. Yet it is not so easy to understand what brings about changes

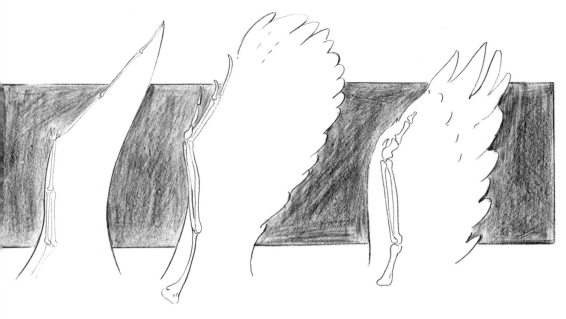

Pterodactyl   *Archaeopteryx*   *Bird*

in bodily structure which may take a million or ten million years to produce. We can only guess at these changes by studying and dating, insofar as we can, the layers of rock laid down in age after age.

Until 1861, little was known of the origin of birds. In that year a great event took place in a quarry in Solenhofen, Bavaria. This quarry, which had been in use for many years, produced a very fine-grained limestone, a stone remarkably useful in the process of lithography, which is the art of putting printed words or pictures on suitable stone covered with a greasy substance, and taking off the impression on paper. The stone of Solenhofen was laid down in the form of very fine mud some 140 or 150 million years ago, mud which remained undisturbed until it was covered by a protecting surface of other material, piled so high that the mud, with

37

its layers undisturbed, was flattened to a smooth hard rock. Yet the mud itself was not all that was hardened and preserved. Dragonflies and other insects had settled on the silt and, unable to escape, had been flattened and preserved, their delicate wing membranes unchanged.

Frequently, in taking slabs of stone from the quarry, these ancient forms appeared when the slabs were split. One day a scientist named Haberlein was studying the floor of the quarry. He stopped in amazement when he came upon the perfect imprint of a feather engraved upon the stone which had held the image for perhaps 140 million years. This was the feather of no known bird. Nor had it been known that at the time the Solenhofen stone was deposited anything with feathers existed. The discovery of this remarkable picture of a tiny fragment of the past led to further search of the quarry. A little later in the same year, as slabs of stone were being cut and split for shipment to the printing trade and for use as roofing slates, the secret of the mysterious feather was revealed. Only a short distance from where the feather had been found lay, flattened and badly broken, the almost complete skeleton of an unknown flying creature, a creature with leg and wing bones like a bird's but with a long, feathered tail with bones in it. But for the feathers it would have been more like a lizard's tail. What was most extraordinary was the fact that the creature's upper jaw had thirteen rows of unmistakable teeth and the lower jaw three cone-shaped teeth, all planted in definite sockets.

Here, for the first time, was a link between the birds and the reptiles. Shortly after its discovery, scientists described the new bird-reptile. The name given to it by a German scholar, von Meyer, was *Archaeopteryx lithographica*, meaning, if translated freely, "ancient wing from the lithographic stone." Most scientists agreed that *Archaeopteryx* was a bird, not a reptile. No one,

Fossilized remains of
Archaeopteryx and
reconstruction

Skull of
Archaeopteryx

however, could tell from the skeleton what its manner of living might have been nor what the ancestors, who linked it with the reptiles, may have been. Certainly this bird could fly, not merely glide, and it must have been at home in trees, for, in addition to its wings, it had three separate clawed fingers which would have been a help in climbing. In most modern birds (there are some exceptions) the fingers of the "hand" have become merged with the wing.

How *Archaeopteryx'* power of flight was developed is still a mystery and how the modern bird, which could fly rings around it, grew out of this ancient creature to such perfect form can only be guessed at. One theory of the origin of flight is that small dinosaurs with very short forelegs and long, powerful hind ones had the habit of running on their hind legs, pawing the air, as if swimming through it, with their forelegs. Over a vast stretch of time this habit could have caused in some way a flattening and widening of the hands, with perhaps a fraying of the edges. Since feathers are merely a development out of scales it is not impossible that in the course of ages a growth of feathers on the outer edges of the hands could have been sufficient to make the creature's pawing of the air effective. This increased use of the forelegs could have caused increased muscular development in what in a man we would call the chest. Eventually the changing, feathered forelegs could have become a real help to the creature, even such a help that their pressure on the air could have lifted him off the ground and permitted the beginning of flight. This is only a theory, but although unproved, will serve as an explanation until scientists provide a better one.

Whatever the steps leading up to it, *Archaeopteryx* had the power of flight and the power of flight led to the final development of birds. In Eocene times (Eocene being the "dawn recent" period referred to in Chapter 8) the birds became more numerous than all the varieties of mammals and reptiles combined. It is thought that all of our familiar birds reached their present development from 11 to 25 million years ago. About a million years ago, when the great masses of ice swept over large areas of the Northern Hemisphere, and later, perhaps 500,000 years ago when man, the destructive one, appeared on earth, the birds began to decline. Birds lived for millions of years without man, but man has never lived without birds. He may have to if he keeps on doing to the earth's surface and its wild inhabitants what he has been doing to them in the the last few thousand years.

It was not man, however, who brought about the extinction of *Archaeopteryx*. Indeed it was man, with his curiosity and inventiveness, who found and understood that 140-million-year-old skeleton. It is to be hoped that he will choose to preserve and cherish the descendants of that ancient creature.

6.

Fossils on Ice

THE MAMMOTH AS HE WAS IN LIFE

THE NOTION that great creatures out of the past which have never been seen by civilized man may still be found in some remote and inaccessible part of the earth is very hard to get out of men's minds. Perhaps this is because there is some truth in this notion, as is indicated by at least one story in this book. Animals thought to be extinct have a way of appearing, just as do some of those long believed to be a creature of legend only, like the okapi of Africa.

More than 250 years ago a Russian traveler named Ludloff reported that he had seen some bones which the people of Siberia called "mamantu." This creature, which the natives of northern Asia believed to be still in existence although they had never seen it alive, was presumed to be a gigantic mole living all its life underground and dying immediately if by chance it became exposed to air and light. There was no other way, the Siberians thought, of explaining two apparently contradictory facts: first, that no one had ever seen a live mamantu and, second, that innumerable people

42

had seen dead ones or parts of dead ones, apparently struck down as they came too near the surface.

At the end of the seventeenth century very few knew anything about any but existing animals. Ludloff's story about the great bones passed, with the name *mamantu*, into the then rather imaginative annals of natural history. The name became somewhat altered in going from one country and one scientist to another until Baron Cuvier, the great French naturalist, set it down in the early nineteenth century as "mammouth." This became, when it entered the English language, "mammoth." Although we now call very large things mammoth, it is obvious that the mammoth, although it was large, was not called mammoth because of its size.

Nor was the mammoth either a mole or a dweller underground. He was a real flesh and blood creature which lived, not only in Siberia but in parts of Europe and North America. The mammoth

Primitive drawings of mammoths

bones which were found in Europe were sometimes, not illogically, thought to be the remains of the elephants which Hannibal brought with him when he came from Africa to harry the Romans. In some regions they were thought to be proof of the former existence of giants. Yet the primitive men who lived in the caves of southern Europe thousands of years before there was a Carthaginian or a Roman had no doubt of the existence of the mammoth. They had seen him and they drew pictures of him, on the walls of caves and sometimes in delicate engraving on pieces of his own tusks. These pictures show the mammoth to be a long-haired elephant with extremely elongated, elaborately curved tusks.

In 1799, it was reported that an entire mammoth, skin, flesh, and bones, had been found frozen in the permanent ice near the Lena River in Siberia, where it had been for thousands of years. The man who found the body chopped out the tusks and sold them for ivory. As the exposed carcass thawed, bears, wolves, and foxes fed upon it. Not until it was almost a skeleton did anyone with scientific interest reach it and try to save it. What was left was taken to St. Petersburg and mounted in the museum there. Since the tusks were missing, others had to be provided and when they were added to the skeleton they were set into the animal's skull on the wrong sides—in other words, with the tips of the tusks pointing outward instead of inward. For more than a hundred years it was supposed that this was the way in which mammoth tusks grew.

In spite of the evidence of antiquity in the Lena River mammoth, rumors persisted throughout the nineteenth century that the great creature might still be found alive in the forests of Siberia or Alaska. The northern mammoth, which belongs to the elephant family, is called *Elephas primigenius*. The rumor that mammoths

C. H. Townsend

still existed in Alaska seemed, for a time in the last part of the nineteenth century, to have been proved true.

When the U. S. Revenue Cutter *Corwin*, in the course of her patrol of the north Alaskan coast, headed for Kotzebue Sound, a spot where many scattered mammoth bones had been found, she had on board a naturalist of the United States Fish Commission. The *Corwin* stopped at Cape Prince of Wales, the nearest point to Siberia, and about 150 miles southwest of Kotzebue. Here some Eskimos came aboard with mammoth bones to sell. When Dr. C. H. Townsend, the naturalist, asked the natives if any of these great creatures were alive in the forests inland from their homes, the Eskimos shook their heads and said no, that they had all died long ago, so long ago that none knew what the complete mam-

45

moth looked like. They wanted to know if Dr. Townsend could describe it. The *Corwin's* library carried a book on geology in which was a picture of the skeleton of the mammoth which had been taken from the Lena River to St. Petersburg almost a hundred years earlier. Townsend had worked at an establishment in Rochester, New York, which specialized in mounting animals and making models of extinct specimens for museums. He had been present when a full-size model of the mammoth had been made. He was therefore able to draw a sketch of the animal as it must have appeared when alive. He gave this sketch to the Eskimos and one of them made a copy of the illustration of the skeleton in the *Corwin's* geology book.

The Eskimos are great travelers and these two drawings went with the Prince of Wales people wherever they went. Other Eskimos copied them on caribou antlers, walrus tusks, and anything else suitable. A newspaper man who had no knowledge of Dr. Townsend's visit with the Prince of Wales Eskimos noticed, on a journey into Alaska, that the Eskimos seemed to have a good knowledge of the appearance and habits of the mammoth. Remembering the cave paintings and drawings of the mammoth which early men in southern Europe had left behind them, the journalist assumed that the Eskimos too must have had firsthand knowledge of the great beast. He came back and wrote a story for his paper saying that undoubtedly the mammoth was still alive in Alaska.

This report was reprinted widely and a story based upon it appeared in *McClure's Magazine* for October, 1899—a tale which, while it was plainly listed as fiction, was taken as truth. The author, unfortunately, said in his piece that the stuffed remains of the mammoth, the killing of which he described, were to be seen in the museum of the Smithsonian Institution in Washington. The fact that the museum had no such specimen did not affect those who thought the story in *McClure's* was true. They continued to believe that the mammoth could be found alive in Alaska. No one, in spite of the fact that Alaska has now been thoroughly explored, has yet seen a living mammoth there.

A few years after the *McClure's* story had appeared, it was reported from Russia that the complete and lifelike carcass of a genuine mammoth had been found frozen in the ice on the Berezovka River in Siberia, sixty miles north of the Arctic Circle and some 800 miles west of Cape Prince of Wales. Although the body had been discovered in 1900, it was not until April, 1901, that the Academy of Sciences at St. Petersburg was notified of the find. It was not until May, 1901, that the Academy was able to send an expedition to find, preserve, and bring home the body. The expedition got within striking distance of the discovery in September of 1901, when they learned that the finder of the carcass, who believed that it had first been exposed by melting of the ice and slipping of the cliff in which it was frozen, as much as a year before he found it, had been ill and unable to go back to the site to take steps to keep it from decaying. This was discouraging news. The members of the expedition remembered what had happened to the mammoth discovered on the Lena River 100 years before.

The banks of the Berezovka River are, on the side on which the mammoth was found, quite steep. They consist of a wall of ice on top of which is a layer of earth, rocks, and roots penetrated by plates of ice a foot or so thick. Out of this four- to six-foot depth of soil grows the Siberian forest. During the short summer there are heavy rains which tend to wash parts of the upper crust of earth, including stones and the trunks of trees, down the steep bank, melting and wearing away some of the ice wall. During one

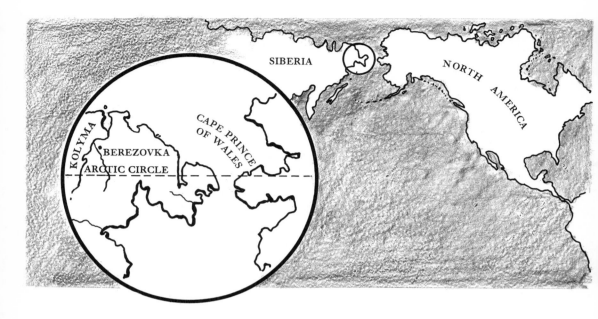

of these summer slides, probably in 1899, the wearing away of the cliff exposed to the air the head of a great mammoth which had been buried there thousands of years before.

Two of the natives of the region who had returned with the discoverer to look at the exposed head removed the huge, gracefully curved tusks and carried them into the town of Kolyma, where they sold them for ivory. The man who bought the tusks went back to look at the buried carcass and, after confirming the fact that it was a great scientific discovery, reported it to St. Petersburg. Unfortunately this man, who removed sample pieces of skin from the head and right thigh and took out a portion of the stomach, did not see to it that the exposed parts of the body were reburied before he left it. The result was that by the time the men from the Russian Academy of Sciences reached the spot, natural decay and the attacks of wild animals had damaged the head and back severely.

Nevertheless, when the expedition stood before the remains, they were vividly impressed, both by a horrible smell and by the sight of a great beast whose real nature had heretofore only been guessed at by modern man. The animal lay as it must have fallen thousands of years ago, its forelegs (the right one broken) struggling to drag its heavy body out of the crevasse into which it had tumbled. One hip and several ribs were broken. The task of escaping from the pit had been too great for the injured animal and it died of exhaustion even before it could swallow all the food which was found between its teeth. After its death the ground about it was washed into the pit and over the carcass, gradually freezing solid and remaining so until the cycles of weather were

Reconstruction of mammoth as found in Siberia

again able to thaw and wash away part of the covering of the great beast's grave.

We now know what *Elephas primigenius* really looked like. We know that this one died in the spring, for the plants and leaves which were found between his teeth and in his great stomach were plants such as are found today in spring in the wild tangle of the north Siberian forest. We know that the great beast was covered with bristly rusty-dark brown hair as much as sixteen inches long. Beneath this outer coat was an undercoat, from ten to twelve inches long, of softer hair the color of camel's hair. The tail, which was shorter than a mammoth's tail had been thought to be, was tipped with an eight- or nine-inch long tuft of hard, bristly hair. The fleshy part of the tail, about a foot around at its base, was little more than a foot long.

The Berezovka mammoth had obviously died in a fall, as no doubt many others did, but what caused the destruction of the entire race? The hairy coat suggests that they were well able to stand the cold. If there were men in Siberia when *Elephas primigenius* lived there, they were probably outnumbered by the mammoth and could not have destroyed them all with any weapons known to primitive society. That there was food in plenty is proved by the great quantity taken from the stomach of the Berezovka specimen. Whatever the reason, it is certain that no mammoth remains alive today.

7.

A Trap for the Past
THE LA BREA TAR PITS OF CALIFORNIA

TWO HUNDRED YEARS AGO when Don Gaspar de Portolá traveled through California, he did not find the maze of superhighways, people, and chemicals suspended in heavy air which now form the City and County of Los Angeles. Northwest of what is now the center of the vast city and a little beyond the present Hollywood, he crossed a wide plain, north and west of which were mountains. In this plain he and his men saw what he described as pools of pitch. He wrote in his account of his journey that the pitch flowed, melted, "from underneath the earth." As he seems to have experienced several earthquake shocks during his presence in the region, he wondered if they could be connected with the welling up of the melted pitch.

Some 20 years later, after the *pueblo*, or town, called *Nuestra Señora la Reina de los Angeles* (Our Lady the Queen of the Angels) had been founded, another exploring Spaniard passed through and reported more than twenty springs of liquid petroleum and pitch. In some places he said that there were many pools in which bubbles and blisters continually formed and exploded. He saw animals struggling in these pools and found along the edges the bones of others which had been swallowed by the sticky substance and later cast up out of the depths. Some of these José Martinez took away with him.

In spite of the fact that the village of Los Angeles grew and prospered, no one seems to have paid much attention to the deposits of pitch until the middle of the nineteenth century, although the Spaniards gave the name "brea" to the sticky stuff, which was made of half liquid asphaltum mixed with sand and dust.

When a survey was made for the Pacific Railroad, a decade after the United States had acquired California, the brea deposits were again noticed but not investigated. In 1865, Mr. J. D. Whitney, the California State Geologist (after whom the highest mountain in the United States south of the Canadian border was named) again reported that bones of "cattle and birds" had been found in the pits of tar. Not until 1875 were these bones recognized as fossils. William Denton, who published an article on them in that year, did not seem to make much impression on the scientific world. His work was soon forgotten. Major Henry Hancock, who owned the ranch on which the pools of pitch were located—it was called the Rancho La Brea—had found a strange tooth near the pools. This he gave to Denton, who described it in his article as having come from the jaw of a sabre-toothed cat.

Not until 1905, after a visit to La Brea by W. W. Orcutt of Los Angeles, did it occur to anyone that the bones found in the tar pits might be prehistoric. Orcutt and Frank M. Anderson visited the strange spot again in the same year and took away with them the skull of a sabre-tooth, the jaws of a huge wolf, and several bones of a peculiar kind which only could have come from a giant ground sloth. Orcutt and Anderson gave this material to Dr. John C. Merriam of the University of California who, being a trained palaeontologist, immediately saw the importance of La Brea as a clue to the mystery of vanished life. He lost no time in getting permission from the owner of La Brea to excavate the tar pits of the Rancho.

In 1906 the University of California began to dig. By that time a large oil field called the Salt Lake field had been opened up between La Brea and the Santa Monica Mountains, which rose from the plain about three miles to the north. At some time between half a million and a million years ago, there was a violent movement of the earth's crust which tilted the layers of ancient sedimentary rock and exposed them to the action of rain and wind, and left broken fissures through which the oil, formed from the sinking to the bottom of the sea of countless marine organisms, could escape upwards. The age of these folded and broken layers of rock can be determined. The upper layers must have been laid down less than a million years ago.

Over these rocks there is a deep deposit of material—clay, sand, and rubble—which has not been disturbed. Since this is on top of the disturbed rocks, it must be younger than they are, which means that it may be between 500,000 and 750,000 years old. That is quite old as we think of age, but not in terms of the total age of the earth, which we now believe to be something like four and a half billion years, perhaps more.

When the University of California started digging in the tar-filled chimneys and fissures of the upper layer of earth at La Brea, no one knew what to expect. In the first few feet there was little that could not be found living or growing above ground in that part of California in 1906. Then as the sticky stuff was scooped

Some of the beasts that lived near the La Brea tar pits

and shovelled out at greater depth, the relics of the past began to grow more numerous and more ancient. At one point, in a pit only three by six feet and eight feet deep, were found the complete skeletons of thirteen animals. These were not animals which would have been familiar to the Californians of the eighteenth century and were familiar to the Californians of the twentieth century only as the fossils of extinct creatures.

Fifty thousand years ago the level of the land in the plain between the Santa Monica Mountains and the sea was somewhat lower than it is now, and it is probable that the pools and pits of pitch were larger and more active than are those which remain today. Yet the climate, if we are to judge by the remains of trees and plants found in the brea, can only have been slightly more humid. In the layers of sand and rubble which at La Brea have accumulated since the middle of the Pleistocene period (the name comes from two Greek words meaning "most new, or recent") there is no sign of any great catastrophe or sudden change in the surface of the earth which could have accounted for the extinction of the many forms of life found there. Yet the majority of them no longer exist.

The region surrounding the La Brea tar pits has probably changed relatively little since the late Pleistocene days. What is now Los Angeles County was not very much affected by the advance and retreat, over a period of many tens of thousands of years, of the great ice sheets of the north and east. It was a region of pine, cypress, juniper, and oak, probably widely scattered, and with many fairly open areas of brush bordering depressions which were ponds and marshes in the rainy season.

Great herds of grazing animals of many kinds found sustenance there, and they were followed and preyed upon by many flesh-eating creatures. The excavations at La Brea enable us to see, as

Giant condor

if we were there in a hunter's blind watching their behavior, what took place in the neighborhood of the tar pits. Here, perhaps lured by poor eyesight which could not distinguish between the glossy sheen of pitch and the bright shine of water, some great beast, possibly a mammoth with long, in-curving tusks, or a smaller mastodon, stepped into the edge of a tar pool and, trying to test it with his trunk, was caught fast. Struggling to escape, he toppled forward and became mired, his great bulk slowly sinking in the black tar. His screaming trumpetings attracted the giant birds of prey—eagles, condors, vultures, and one, greatest of all, which scientists have called *Teratornis*. The great dire wolf, the sabre-toothed cat, and an immense lion stalked the helpless creature in the tar. Their hunger got the better of their judgment. The birds of prey swooped in to snatch at the flesh not yet swallowed by the pitch and, banking too sharply, caught a wing in the sticky substance and were in turn dragged down. The powerful sabre-tooth, which has been called a tiger but was more like a huge, knife-jawed lynx, thrust his great neck forward, sinking the blades of his jaws into the flesh buried in the pitch. He could not keep his forefeet out of the trap and began to sink as he writhed and struggled. The dire wolf was unable to learn from what he saw that here was disaster rather than a feast. He, too, snarling and howling, sank slowly out of sight.

Year after year, century after century, millenium after millenium, this scene was repeated with other actors. Packed together, as their flesh disintegrated in the heavy pitch and their bones became loosened, all those unfortunate creatures who came to the treacherous pools sank into oblivion in the upwelling tar. Yet their oblivion was not permanent.

When the University of California began its work at La Brea, it uncovered unmistakable evidence of the power of the pitch. More than that, it disclosed the skeletons, perfectly preserved by the oil which had destroyed their flesh, the leaves and branches and trunks of some two hundred different animals and plants, represented by many thousands of individuals, giving a panorama of the succession of life from the late Pleistocene to today. Such a view could not have been found in any other known place on earth.

Today the tar pits of La Brea are enclosed in beautiful Hancock Park, adjoining Wilshire Boulevard in Los Angeles. The park is being planted, so far as is possible, with the varieties of trees, shrubs, and plants which are known to have grown in the vicinity during the long Ice Age of the Pleistocene period. Many of the pits have dried up and become grown over, but some are left, in which ground squirrels and other small animals are even now entrapped. In the northwestern corner of the park one large pit has been surrounded by a stone-canopied building within which a staircase descends to a railed observation walk. Here the visitor can stand and look, perhaps unbelieving, at the past.

Within the railed enclosure the black and sticky tar still lies bubbling. In the midst of it is a huge heap of blackened, jumbled bones, left by the excavators exactly as it was found. Here can be made out the skulls of mastodon and extinct wolf, the hip bones of the giant ground sloth, the ribs of a great ancestor of the bison, fragments of camel and the huge, short-faced bear, the crushed skeletons of many small mammals and birds. Here is the past, trapped for our understanding.

It is at the same time an ugly and a beautiful sight, beautiful because it shows with such precision and completeness the details of a long-lost chapter in the history of life.

8.

Not All Prehistoric Creatures Had Descendants

EDWARD COPE'S WEIRD BEAST

LONG, LONG AGO—perhaps 50 million years—when the shallow seas which covered most of what is now dry land had receded and the surface of the earth, in places where it was under pressure, had begun to buckle and rise, the dinosaurs, gigantic and small, had disappeared. Where the Alps of Europe now stand were beaches washed by warm waves. Luxurious vegetation covered the countryside to within a few hundred miles of the North Pole. In the American West, where the Rockies now tower up to 14,000 feet, there were only ranges of low ridges covered with open forest.

The land rose slowly during the 30 million years of what is known as the Eocene, or "dawn recent," period and the mammals (among which many million years later man came to be numbered), which had begun as a few tiny creatures during the Age of Reptiles, had plenty of time to develop many new forms. Many of these were grazing animals browsing the lush vegetation of the hills and river valleys. Many were destined never to know man, the late-comer who was to make such a mark upon the earth that no natural catastrophe can ever erase it. For thousands of years man knew nothing of these predecessors.

The hills of southern Wyoming and northern Utah were built up, layer upon layer, over the dry remains of Cretaceous seas. (Cretaceous, as already indicated, is a word taken from the Latin word for chalk, a material made of countless tiny shells of organisms known as *foraminifera*. Chalk is usually found where the shallow seas of the Age of Reptiles used to be some 70 million years ago.) It was upon uplands beneath which the giants of those ancient seas were buried that the mammals of the Eocene period wandered about for millions of years. They, too, were destined to be buried where they had lived. During the later Eocene period, perhaps 45 or 50 million years ago, the shifting, shrinking, cracking, and upthrusting of the earth's crust as the western mountains rose toward their present heights produced great heat below the surface. The lower rocks burned in this heat and their ashes were forced up and out into the air to drift over the land and fall in a dry rain of infinitesimal fragments of glassy sand, covering everything for many miles about. Many of the animals which lived in the region were able to escape but many were not. They were buried as the great sea creatures of millions of years earlier had been buried in the sediments of their seas.

Until the last half of the nineteenth century no bones of the creatures of the Eocene period had been found. Not even the keenest of scientists could guess what these strange beasts might have been like. None of those travelers through the West who looked from their wagons and early railroad cars at the tortured and pockmarked landscape of southern Wyoming and northern Utah guessed that the history of the Eocene lay buried there, and was in some places exposed to the light of day by the cutting work of rivers and the force of fierce winds. Some pioneers reported that in their journeys westward they had seen great bones, but these had been taken to be relics of animals drowned in the Biblical flood which Noah built his ark to escape.

It happened that two men, one born in Philadelphia and the other in Lockport, New York, finished their education at about the time the Union Pacific Railroad was completed in 1867. Each of these young men had been drawn through a passion for nature to study the natural history of ages long gone. In other words, each had become a palaeontologist.

Edward Drinker Cope was a Philadelphia Quaker who had been something of a prodigy in his youth. He was able to draw skillfully and well when he was ten years old, and by the time he was fourteen he was well read in the scientific literature of birds, snakes, insects, and fishes. When he was twenty he studied anatomy at the University of Pennsylvania under the great Joseph Leidy. In 1861 and 1862 he studied in the Smithsonian Institution at Washington. In 1863, when the Civil War was at its height, Cope's father, who was a better Quaker than his son, sent the young man abroad for two years in order to keep him out of the fighting. Edward met and studied with some of the leading European scientists. Although his unconventional studies brought him no college degree, he had no trouble, when he returned to the United States in 1864, in getting an appointment as Professor of Zoology at Haverford College. It was at this time that the young professor began to use his spare time for hunting fossils. He soon found this more interesting than teaching. As it was also more time-consuming, he resigned his post at Haverford and devoted

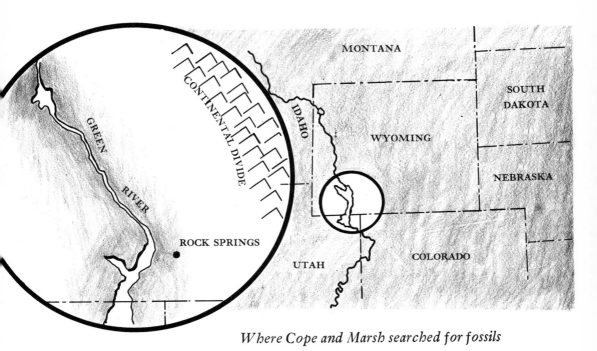

Where Cope and Marsh searched for fossils

himself to what was to be his life work.

Cope knew the geological history of the American West. He believed that a man might find in Kansas, Colorado, Utah, and Wyoming, traces of the ancient life which had lived in that region through the millions of years of the rising and falling of the earth's crust, of alternating sea and land. Edward Cope sold the farm which his father had given him hoping that the young man would live on it, and headed for Kansas.

He found trouble ahead. There was another palaeontologist, Othniel Charles Marsh, he who was born at Lockport, New York, who had completed a more formal education than Cope's at about the same time although he was nine years older. Marsh had a very rich uncle and a firm belief that he should be permitted to get whatever he wanted. He, too, knew that fossil-hunting was to be his life work and, like Cope, he knew that the place to look was

63

the Western plains and the eastern slopes of the Rocky Mountains. Before Cope got started, Marsh had been to Kansas and begun digging. Although most of western Kansas was public land, Marsh believed that since he had been first in the field no one else had a right to dig there. When Cope went to Kansas, Marsh regarded the younger man as a trespasser and did everything he could to make things difficult for him.

Serious scientists though they both were, Marsh and Cope fought like children in temper tantrums for the next thirty years. Yet, since they were serious scientists, well trained and brilliant in thought and action, each of them was enormously successful.

On his first trip to Kansas, Edward Cope, with his party of seven men, two wagons, and fourteen pack mules, struck westward over the Kansas prairies through herds of bison which galloped off in clouds of dust. The flat prairie grass gave way, at first, to rolling gravelly hills and, still farther west, to a country of small canyons worn into the yellow sandstone by millions of years of rain. In some places the yellow striated bluffs were so deeply cut that older blue sandstone showed beneath the outer layers, marking the transition between different periods of time.

It was rough, dry country where, in the 1890s, sandstorms took the place of rain, the grit-laden wind biting at the ancient bluffs and making it almost impossible to breathe. The men had to wear handkerchiefs over their noses and mouths. The horses and mules could only stand with drooping heads, their rear ends to the wind, taking the biting wind-drift of the sand.

During one of these storms, Cope, peering through two slits in the handkerchief tied over his face, climbed down a bluff toward the base of blue sandstone. He was discouraged and disheartened, for it was almost impossible to see anything. He reached out to steady himself against the rock as he stepped down into a dry

Edward D. Cope   *Mosasaur*

stream bed, and suddenly stopped in his tracks. There, a little above his head, projected from the rock the huge skull of what was undoubtedly a true sea serpent of the Cretaceous period. The great creature had been buried in the sand of the early ocean which covered much of the West 70 million years ago. The animal was a *mosasaur* (named after the river Meuse in northeastern France, where the first specimen was found). Although not new to science, lying as it died in the sand of a sea bottom now several thousand feet above sea level, it filled Edward Cope with an excitement which made him forget that he himself was almost being buried in sandy drift. Cope seems to have thought that the creature was a new species, for he gave it a new name—*Liodon dyspelor* Cope. He reported enthusiastically that its head was on one side of the outthrust bluff and its tail on the other. He estimated its length as

65

at least 75 feet, something of an exaggeration as no mosasaur exceeding 45 feet in length has yet been found. In the Cretaceous beds of Kansas, Cope found many fine specimens of extinct sea creatures which he shipped home to his crowded house in Philadelphia.

The following year, again encountering opposition from the imperious Othniel Marsh, Cope went to southern Wyoming, to a region on the Green River known as the Washakie territory. Here he discovered something really new to science. It was an enormous skull, some three feet in length, which must have belonged to an animal twice the size of an elephant. He called it *Eobasileus*, or "dawn king," for it was a representative of a race of mammals of the existence of which no man had been aware, a race which had appeared in Eocene (or "dawn recent") times when that newly-developed form of life, the mammal, was trying

Eobasileus, the "dawn king"

to find the variety most suitable for survival. Cope's *Eobasileus* was one of a group of mammals which lived perhaps 45 or 50 million years ago but turned out to be a step in the wrong direction. They undoubtedly did well for a while, but they did not survive for long enough to become the ancestors of any creature now living. They were at once the dawn and twilight of their own kind.

Eobasileus was one of the strangest creatures that ever lived. His body was enormous, as has been suggested, and bore some resemblance to the elephant family. The head was very much elongated. The teeth were peculiar. Upon the top of the skull were three pairs of bony protruberances both like and unlike horns, which resemble nothing alive today. Cope believed, when he first unearthed the creature's amazing skull, that, like the elephant, it had, in life, carried a long trunk. He drew a sketch of what he thought the animal must have looked like, a portrait which scientists now believe was very far from accurate. Yet the skull, just as Cope found it, is in the collection of the American Museum of Natural History in New York. Had Cope not allowed his enthusiasm for fossil-hunting to overcome his fear of what his rival Othniel Marsh might do to hinder him, and had not Marsh, who found related but slightly different beasts west of the Washakie region, been stimulated by his rivalry, our knowledge of the great freaks of the Eocene world would have been much delayed.

Looking back on the ill-fated bulk of *Eobasileus*, it seems to us that if the conditions under which that creature lived had allowed his brain to develop as readily as the bony structure of his skull, he and his companion beasts known as *Dinocerata* (or "terrible horns") might be alive today. For some reason they did not. *Eobasileus* is now a museum specimen only, a fossil example of what a living creature should not be like.

9.

The Treasure of Chou-K'ou Tien
DRAGON BONES AND PEKING MAN

No INHABITANT of China has ever seen a dragon, but even under the rigid discipline of Chinese Communism there are millions of Chinese who have no doubt whatever that dragons once existed in their great land. The Chinese peasant is certain that the spirits of dragons (and they are benevolent spirits, not like those of European dragons which had to be slain by knights) still exist, and that their bones are scattered over the land waiting to be gathered and ground up into medicinal powders.

Travelers in China, particularly North China, have long known of the shops, which we call drug stores, in which dragon bones in form suitable for medicinal dosage are sold. The continued existence of these shops presupposes an enormous supply of bones. At the beginning of the twentieth century a German scientist named Haberer tried to find out what the bones were and where they came from. He went about among the shops and purchased such unpowdered bones as he was able to find. He obtained enough to convince him that the bones were fossil bones which had been buried in the earth for a long time. Dr. Haberer shipped his collection to a friend in Munich. The friend sorted them out and was able to identify nearly one hundred of them. They were all from extinct animals such as mammoths, mastodons, sabre-tooth tigers, and primitive three-toed horses.

When the Munich scientist's report of these "dragon bones" was published, it made a great many European palaeontologists extremely eager to get to China in order to look for more bones. China, however, with its popular prejudice against outsiders, particularly Europeans, was not an easy place in which to travel. One of the first to be put in a position from which he could study Chinese fossils was a Swedish geologist named J. Gunnar Andersson, who was asked by the Chinese Government to come to China and give the Chinese Geological Survey advice about deposits of minerals and rock formations which might be commercially developed. Dr. Andersson was a palaeontologist on the side, and he had seen the German report on Dr. Haberer's collection of dragon bones. He made up his mind to do a little exploring for his own benefit whenever he got the opportunity.

He began, as Dr. Haberer had done, by buying whatever bones he could find and by writing to missionaries throughout China in the hope that some of them might know where the apparently endless supply of fossils came from. He found out very little but realized that if he had more time he could do better. A friend of Andersson's in Stockholm suggested that an assistant would be the answer. The friend knew just the man, and would get him a two-years' leave of absence and send him to China to join Dr. Andersson's staff. The fortunate young man was an Austrian palaeontologist who had been working at the University of Uppsala. His name was Otto Zdansky.

One of the first things which Zdansky undertook when he joined Andersson was a study of the clues which had come to Andersson but which the Swedish scientist had been unable to follow up. One of these led to the village of Chi-chia K'ou on the Yellow River in northern China, 300 miles west of Peking and 750 miles southeast of The Flaming Cliffs, where Roy Chapman Andrews searched for traces of prehistoric life. Here he found what was really a bone mine, operated by villagers when they were not farming. At first the peasants pretended that they had no idea what Zdansky was talking about. Dr. Zdansky, however, knew that bones from Chi-chia K'ou were regularly sold to drug houses in the great eastern cities. Moreover, he knew what the drug men paid for the bones—never more than a few coppers per bone, no matter how good a specimen it was. By offering the bone miners a considerably higher price, which he could easily afford to do, he was able to overcome their reticence and not only purchase bones but be shown the mine itself.

Chi-chia K'ou is situated on a great plateau between the river and a range of mountains to the east of it. Watercourses originating in these mountains had worn deep, canyon-like gullies in the red clay of the plateau, beneath which a deposit of coal had been laid down in very ancient times. The Chinese villagers had dug small passages into the high cliffs of red clay wherever there was indication of the presence of a pocket of bones. Some of the tunnels, which were only big enough for a man to crawl through, extended as much as 400 feet into the plateau. The miners would crawl into the tunnel carrying a short pick and dragging a primitive cart behind them, lengthening the tunnel and pushing out the debris as they went. When they reached a deposit of bones they loaded up the cart with chunks of bone-bearing clay and pushed it to the entrance. When they reached daylight at the

Excavation at Chou-K'ou Tien

mouth of the tunnel, they cleaned the bones and, if there were any skulls and jaws in the lot, broke them up and extracted the teeth, which were very much in demand among the drug men.

Dr. Zdansky was able to persuade the miners that he would pay twice as much for a skull or jawbone with the teeth still in it as the druggists would pay for the teeth alone. In this way he built up a fine collection of specimens of the remains of prehistoric rhinoceros, elephant, tiger, bear, pig, and giraffe. His success at this fossil mine, although none of the things he had found went as far back as the dinosaur and showed no trace of prehistoric man, excited Dr. Zdansky and led him to continue his explorations. Shortly before Dr. Roy Chapman Andrews was finding dinosaur skeletons in the Gobi Desert, Dr. Zdansky and his Chinese associate Dr. H. C. T'au found dinosaurs in Shantung, south of Peking. These were the first dinosaurs to be found north of the Himalaya Mountains.

Had Dr. Zdansky's leave of absence from Sweden been extended, he might have been the man to make one of the great palaeontological discoveries of the century. One day, after he had returned from the last of his many explorations, Dr. Andersson, his chief, took him and Dr. Walter Granger, palaeontologist from the American Museum of Natural History who had come to China to join the great Central Asiatic Expedition, to visit a quarry 50 miles north of Peking in which "dragon bones" had been found. At Chou-K'ou Tien, the three were examining a column of red clay which had been left untouched in the center of the limestone quarry. A Chinese villager who seemed rather apprehensive about their attention to the bones which could be seen sticking out of the column, told them that if they wanted to find bones he could show them a much better place. Moreover, it would be a place which was not so dangerously haunted by the

72

spirits of evil foxes as the red column in the quarry was. The peasant led them over some low hills to a smaller quarry. At the back of this was a wall of limestone in which there appeared the opening of a cave. The cave seemed to be almost completely filled by the same red clay which composed the column in the larger quarry which they had left. Dr. Andersson and his companions saw immediately that the clay was crammed with fossils. Eagerly the visitors began breaking out what they could and wrapping them for later study. They returned on the following day and continued to dig, finding many animals similar to those which Zdansky had found in the plateau near the Yellow River—animals dating back perhaps from half a million to a million years.

Dr. Andersson and Dr. Granger had to return to Peking after a few days—Dr. Granger to join the expedition which was headed for the Gobi Desert in search of, among other things, traces of ancient man, traces which, as it turned out, they never found.

Dr. Zdansky remained at Chou-K'ou Tien and continued to dig. He was very excited when he found some flakes of quartz which seemed to him to have been shaped for use as cutting tools. Dr. Andersson, who returned one day for a brief visit to the cave, agreed with Zdansky and told him that he had a premonition that very ancient human remains would be found if Zdansky kept on digging until he reached the cave bottom. Zdansky did keep on, but ran into difficulties. The cave was much larger than he had thought and as it grew deeper, masses of material from the walls threatened to cave in. Scaffolding and shoring—posts and planks to hold back the loose material—were plainly necessary if work was to continue. No such equipment was available and there was no money to buy it. Zdansky finally had to stop digging and return to Peking. He occasionally got some backing and returned to the Chou-K'ou Tien cave for further work. Most of the material which was dug out was shipped to Sweden for analysis.

One day, word came from Sweden that among the material sent there for study the scientists examining it had found two human teeth, one from an adult and one from a child. Dr. Andersson had photographs of the teeth sent to him. He made slides of the photographs and gave a lecture in which he announced to the world that the first proof of the existence of prehistoric man in Asia had been found. In spite of this news, which should have been world-shaking, the world was not very much stirred. The newspapers which had made much of the notion that Dr. Roy Chapman Andrews was in China looking for the so-called "Missing Link" between man and the lower animals, paid little attention to the Chou-K'ou Tien teeth. Scholars warned Andersson that the teeth might perhaps not be human at all.

In spite of this, Dr. Andersson and a Canadian physician, Dr. Davidson Black, who was teaching at the medical school in Peking, persuaded the Rockefeller Foundation to put up money to continue the excavation at Chou-K'ou Tien. The work was to be under the supervision of the Chinese Geological Survey, and all material excavated was to be studied and reported on by Dr. Black. Unfortunately, at this point the earnest and eager Dr. Zdansky found that his leave could not be extended. On the verge of triumph in China, he had to return to Sweden. Another Swedish scientist, Birger Bohlin, was sent to replace him and to work with the new Chinese leader of the project, Dr. Ting.

After five months of digging, the political situation became so bad that the work at the cave was threatened and eventually had to stop. The Chinese were returning to their ancient hatred of foreigners and developing a strong sense of nationalism. This did not, however, prevent wars among themselves, nor the disturbing operations of organized bandits and guerillas who sometimes threw hand grenades into the quarry at Chou-K'ou Tien just to see the workmen jump.

Three days before Birger Bohlin decided that his work must stop, he found a third human tooth. He stuffed it in his pocket and carried it to Peking to Dr. Davidson Black, who was already convinced that ancient man would be found in Chou-K'ou Tien cave. He considered Bohlin's find, which was the tooth of a child, to be sufficient added evidence to make it certain that a new form of man had been discovered. On the strength of the three teeth found in the cave he gave to this new man the name *Sinanthropus pekinensis*, meaning roughly "Chinese man of Peking."

So, although Roy Chapman Andrews had planned to search for ancient man in the very area where work had begun by Otto

Peking man and skull

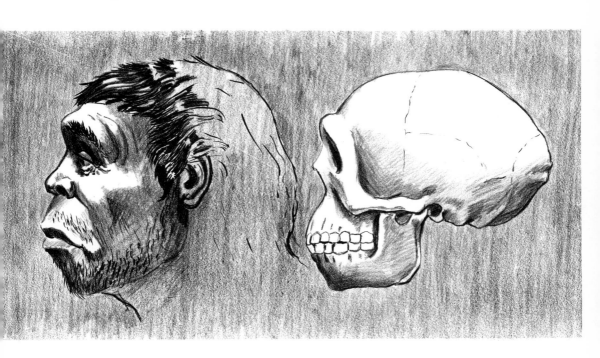

Zdansky, the American scientist was kept from being the first to find Peking Man by the request of the Chinese Geological Survey that the Americans keep out of the area in which its scientists were working. A year later, in 1928, when the political situation was temporarily better, Dr. Bohlin and two Chinese assistants, Yang Ching-chien and P'ei Wen-chung, resumed work at Chou-K'ou Tien. The team had great luck almost from the start, finding many human teeth, several parts of skulls, and a section of an adult human jaw containing several teeth. A fragment of the chin bone of a child made it possible to compare the young of Peking man with a modern Chinese child. There was no doubt that the Chou-K'ou Tien man was more human than ape, yet of great antiquity.

In 1929, Dr. Bohlin joined an expedition to Chinese Turkestan and left P'ei Wen-Chung, better known as Dr. W. C. Pei, in charge, working with money supplied by the Rockefeller Foundation. Dr. Pei reached a depth of 60 feet in the cave and at that level found two smaller connected caves, one of which could be easily worked. In this the Chinese scientist found ashes of hearth fires, pieces of burned wood and bone, and fragments of the skeletons of animals which the inhabitants of the cave had used for food. Suddenly Dr. Pei saw before him a curved object, partly free and partly embedded in rock. This, he knew, could be nothing other than the skull of Peking Man. Dr. Pei took the skull and its attached piece of rock to the Medical School in Peking and began the delicate task of separating the skull from the rock. This took him four months, which seems a long time until it is realized that it took more than 500,000 years for the skull and the rock to become joined together.

Between 1929 and 1932, several more parts of skulls and one that was almost complete were found. The growing collection from Chou-K'ou Tien had become the finest collection of parts of ancient man available to scholars. The Chinese Geological Sur-

76

vey purchased the site of the Chou-K'ou Tien cave in order to keep out dragon bone hunters, and the Chinese Government, aided by the Rockefeller Foundation, decided to continue the work.

Dr. Davidson Black, who had been entrusted with the preparation and care of the Chou-K'ou Tien material, wore himself out working on it and died in 1934. Dr. Franz Weidenreich, a German scholar and a student of the human body, was asked to take over Dr. Black's work. One of the first things Dr. Weidenreich did was make casts of all the important fragments of skull, tooth, and bone which had been found. Meantime, China was in a bad state. The Japanese invaded Manchuria and threatened still more of the ancient nation. The pressure on foreigners became intense. Dr. Weidenreich left for America after having the Chou-K'ou Tien material packed in cases. The doctor took with him the casts he had made and left the cases of the original material with the Chinese Government. The government, unable to be sure that it could remain in Peking, turned the precious cases over to the U. S. Marine guard at the American Legation. The Japanese, however, invaded Peking, took the Legation Marines prisoner, and seized all the property in the legation.

The United States Marine Corps, which does not like to be frustrated, assigned an officer, after the defeat of Japan in 1945, to look for *Sinanthropus pekinensis* in China, Japan, and the Far Eastern islands. No trace of the cases containing the treasures has ever been found. Peking man, after his brief sojurn in the light after something not much less than a million years, was never seen again. The casts of the specimens which Dr. Franz Weidenreich made and took out of China with him are the only evidence that Peking Man ever existed. The Chinese, however, are still searching—successfully, according to report, although they are now quite secretive about their scientific work—for more traces of ancient man in their country.

10.

The Mystery of Last Hope Inlet
THE GIANT SLOTH OF PATAGONIA

IN THE SOUTHERNMOST PART of Chile, there is a province called Magallanes, which is the Chilean version of what the bad ear of the English heard as Magellan, the name of the great navigator who tried to sail around the world when it was a real trick to do so. Magellan never got farther than the Philippines, although some of his ships did. He did, however, navigate the strait which now bears his name. The Strait of Magellan, like the province through which it passes, is inhospitable to the traveler—cold, wet, and constantly filled with dangerously shifting winds and currents which raise havoc with ships' rudders.

Although the province of Magallanes is in about the same latitude in the south as the milder region about London, England, is in the north, it is the home of at least a part of one of the few ice caps remaining on earth. Yet most of the western part of the rocky, sparsely inhabited province is heavily forested, the glaciers which flow down from the remains of the old ice sheet often tearing up trees on their way to the sea. Curiously enough, there are parts of this wild region which, although moist enough to support forest growth today, must have been quite dry many thousands of years ago. There are also stretches, except in the neighborhood of the outer western islands, where the climate is still relatively dry. This region, including the southern provinces of Argentina, on the east, is known as Patagonia. If you cannot find Patagonia on the map (and on some maps you will not), it is because the name is an old and purely a descriptive one, not a political name at all. It comes from the name that Magellan gave to the native inhabitants whom he called "patagones," which means "big feet."

In 1896, a dispute between Chile and Argentina over their boundaries in the far south had been settled by being referred to Great Britain for arbitration. In 1897 the line of the proposed boundary in Patagonia was being surveyed and marked. In November of that year, Dr. F. P. Moreno of the boundary survey paid a visit to a field force which was working between the 51st and 52nd degrees of south latitude, between 100 and 150 miles northeast of the western entrance to the Strait of Magellan. Here at the end of a fjord, or rock-walled inlet, called Ultima Speranza (Last Hope)—perhaps because some early explorer had sailed into it when his provisions were exhausted, hoping that it would lead him somewhere—is a small cove, on the eastern shore of which is the tiny settlement of Puerto Consuelo.

The rather steep shores of this cove, which is quite close to the source of the Rio Gallegos, which flows through dry country to the Atlantic, were heavily overgrown with evergreens and beech trees. The region about Consuelo Cove was not one of dripping, fog-haunted forest such as was to be found west of it, but was normally dry and, although wooded in its hilly parts, in climate much more like the pampas (or plain) region on the east side of the Cordillera (or mountain range) which separates the Pacific slope from the Atlantic.

When Dr. Moreno set foot on shore in Consuelo Cove and had time to look around after meeting the party of surveyors which had arrived before him, he found evidence that the region had already been explored by others. On a beech tree not far from the shore he found hanging a rectangular piece of the skin of an animal with longish, tawny yellow hair. The skin was about 19 by 22 inches and varied in thickness from ⅜ to ½ an inch. What chiefly interested Dr. Moreno was the fact that it was obviously a comparatively small fragment of the skin of a huge animal, that it appeared to have upon it the faded traces of blood stains, and that the reverse, or hairless, side of it was a mass of small, embedded fragments of bone of the kind which zoologists call ossicles (little bones).

Now there is only one order of mammal which is known to carry such ossicles in its skin. That order is the order of *Edentata* (or toothless ones, although only the anteaters of this group are toothless). In this order are included, in addition to the anteaters, the armadillos, tree sloths, and ground sloths. The ground sloths, which are extinct and known only from fossil remains, were huge creatures, the largest of them as bulky as an Indian elephant. They were supposed to have sat on their enormous hind legs, supported by a great tail, and, with claws as big as a one-armed pirate's hook, pulled large treetops down to their mouths so that they might munch the leaves which were thought to be their chief article of food. These creatures, known as *mylodonts* (meaning "teeth like grindstones") did wear, in their thick hides, an armor of small bones.

Since the piece of skin which Dr. Moreno found was still recog-

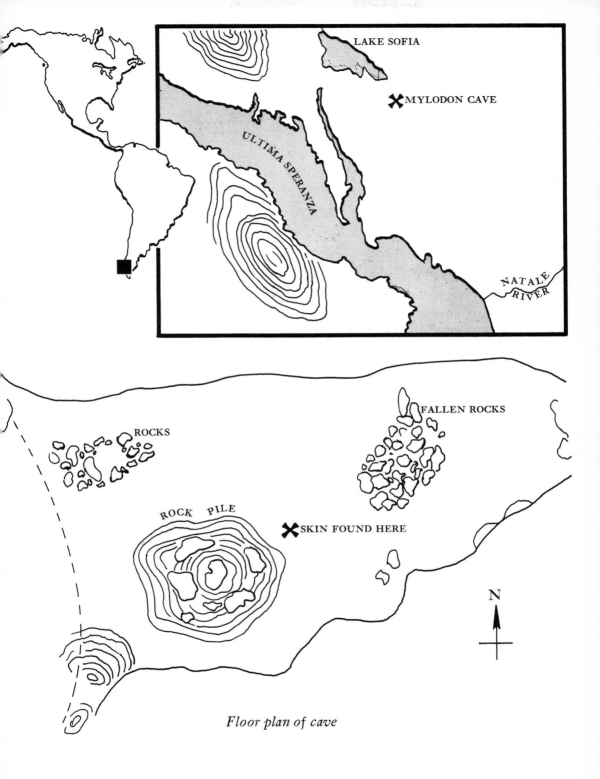

Floor plan of cave

nizable as skin and still retained its hair, the doctor found its presence in Consuelo Cove hard to understand. He knew enough to realize that the embedded small bones should place the wearer of the skin in the family of mylodonts. The skin, however, was relatively fresh and the mylodonts were not. They had been, or were thought to have been, extinct for perhaps 50,000 years. Dr. Moreno's first thought was to make inquiries about his find, which, in its conspicuous position hanging on the Consuelo Cove beech tree, must have been seen by others. He soon learned that the fragment of skin was only a small part of a larger piece which had been discovered in 1895 by a German rancher named Eberhardt in a cave in the cliffs above the cove. One of the sailors on the vessel which had brought Dr. Moreno to Last Hope Inlet said that he had been present when the original discovery was made.

Dr. Moreno was quite excited. He had visions of a great discovery which should make his name remembered by scientists forever. Unfortunately, he was obliged to meet another group of boundary surveyors farther north in a very short time. If he did not get out of the inlet when the weather was favorable he might be much delayed. He had time only to climb, with the sailor, up through the forest to the cave which, to his surprise, was truly enormous. Its entrance formed a great yawning mouth in the western side of a rocky hill some 500 feet above Consuelo Cove. The cavern opening was perhaps 80 or 90 feet high at the central point of its arch and more than 400 feet wide. Trees and bushes grew on the platform before the cave mouth and down into the cave as far as the diminishing light would allow them to. From the ledge at the entrance, Dr. Moreno could see, far to the south, the pampas which descend gradually to the Atlantic. To the west were shining fjords and forested mountains. Between 100 and 200 feet inward from the entrance, Dr. Moreno saw a pile of huge rocks covered with what looked like a pinkish gray dust. The sailor said that the strange skin had been found on the far side of this rock pile which had long ago fallen from the vaulted roof. Dr. Moreno dug a little in the dry leaves and gravel of the vast floor but found nothing of any importance before he had to leave. He gave instructions that some of his men were to remain at the cove and do further digging in the floor of the cavern.

Either because of inexperience, the great size of the cave, or lack of patience, Dr. Moreno's crew found nothing in the course of their digging but the bones of a few quite up-to-date rodents whose skins, had they been preserved, would little more than have covered the palm of a man's hand. Dr. Moreno, meanwhile, had made inquiries and learned that even when the huge original skin, of which he had a fragment, had been found, there had been no bones with it. It had been buried in the dust, rubble, and leaves of the cave floor with nothing to indicate how it got there or what it really was. The doctor decided that he would see to it that further study of the cavern at Consuelo Cove be made.

Meanwhile, the portion of skin which Dr. Moreno had carried away with him came into the hands of Dr. A. Smith Woodward of the Royal Society in London, who studied it with the greatest care. He concluded that it was that of either a Mylodon, differing slightly from known fossil specimens, or a new species which should quite properly have another name. Dr. Woodward said, however, that the right answer to the puzzle must wait for further digging in the cave of Last Hope Inlet.

A Swedish scientist, Erland Nordenskjöld, nephew of the famous Otto Nordenskjöld, did considerable careful excavating in 1899, and was able to establish the fact that there were several distinct layers, which he plotted with some accuracy, underlying the surface of the cave floor. The upper layer contained the bones of animals living in the region at the time of excavation and some signs of human occupation, in the form of charred wood and leaves and branches of trees commonly found near the cave at the time. The middle layer yielded no wood and contained the remains of the guanaco (a relative of the llama) and of an extinct horse. The bottom layer, largely made up of a kind of dung or dry manure at the time unidentified, gave up many bones of extinct animals, among them the giant sloth. Erland Nordenskjöld stopped work in April, 1899, for reasons which are not entirely clear.

While Nordenskjöld was still at Puerto Consuelo, Dr. Rudolph Hauthal of the La Plata Museum in Buenos Aires visited the cave and apparently talked with Nordenskjöld and saw what the Swede had taken from the cave. Hauthal then undertook a week or so of digging on his own, finding another piece of the skin of the Mylodon and additional bones which unquestionably belonged to the giant ground sloth, fossils of which had been found in more than one place on the pampas of Buenos Aires province to the northeast of the great cavern. This species was, at the time, given the name *Gryptotherium* (which seems to mean "curved beast").

This settled the question of the identity of the creature whose skin had been found by Dr. Moreno. Dr. Hauthal's discoveries helped to resolve this problem but raised other questions which seemed even more interesting. To indicate what these were, it is necessary to say exactly what it was that Dr. Hauthal found. First of all he discovered, as Nordenskjöld had before him, a thin layer of ashes, dust, gravel—and the bones of recent animals which he believed had been cracked and broken by man. A little lower down, the character of the cave debris changed, as Nordenskjöld had also found. The third, and bottom, layer of cave flooring was about a yard in thickness. Here there were no branches, no leaves, but, at first, only dried herbs. As Dr. Hauthal and his men dug, it seemed that a part of the cave, a hundred feet farther in, had been walled in by what he felt certain was the work of man. A ridge of rock from 10 to 15 feet high ran almost all the way across the cave between 300 and 400 feet from the entrance. In the vicinity of this wall also were found the bones of a member of the cat family larger than the living South American jaguar and unknown to science, a large extinct and also unknown rodent, and a thigh bone believed to belong to the great, extinct short-faced bear, *Arctotherium*, which was as large as the huge brown bear of Alaska. Most astonishing of all, according to Hauthal, was the fact that this fragment of *Arctotherium* bone seemed to have been cut by man!

As if this discovery of a bear thought to be long extinct, in company with man, thought to be only recently developed, were not enough, the unearthing of the area about the wall in the bottom of the cave produced, in the form of something which seemed to be cut hay and a deep layer of dung (obviously from the giant sloth), apparent evidence that man had kept the huge beast as a domestic animal which he slaughtered and fed upon at will. The revelations of the cave at Consuelo Cove, said Hauthal, indicated either one of two things. Either the race of man in South America was far more ancient than it had been supposed to be, or the era

Short-faced bear

of the extinct horse, the *Arctotherium*, and the giant ground sloth, *Gryptotherium*, extended much nearer to our own times than any man had believed it did.

Even if the condition of the prehistoric skin, bones, and dung (none of which were fossilized in the true sense, the bones retaining their cartilage and traces of sinew and the dung the undecomposed herbs and grasses which the great sloth had eaten) indicates a comparatively recent end to the lives of those concerned, can we believe that the Consuelo cave was inhabited by prehistoric beasts within historic times? It would be hard to do so. It would be equally hard to believe what we should have to believe if Dr. Hauthal's evidence was sound—that man's residence in southern Chile dates back as much as ten, twenty, or thirty thousand years.

So hard was it for some to believe that the great sloth whose skin, still hairy, waved in the 1890s from a tree at the edge of Last Hope Inlet had been dead for more than a man's lifetime of years, that the story got about, fortified by remembered legends of the Tehuelche people, perhaps the last human natives of the region, that *Gryptotherium* was still to be found alive in the Patagonian forests. Needless to say, no trace of a living ground sloth has ever been found, neither footprints—which would be unmistakable, since the creature's great claws forced him to walk on the outer edges of his front feet—nor droppings, nor reports of sightings.

The *Gryptotherium* apparently had been dead for many thousands of years, which is nothing compared with the 70 million years of the supposed extinction of the coelacanth. Yet that monster fish with his leg-bone fins and his prehistoric armor-plate did come to the surface of the sea to confound us.

In the early years of the nineteenth century, Dr. Hauthal's story made a great sensation and, although there was apparently no further scientific digging at the Puerto Consuelo cavern to support his theory, it had its day in the press and then was forgotten.

Scientists, however, did not forget either the giant Mylodon (which is the name now used for the *Gryptotherium*) nor the astonishing cavern in which it had once lived, although they never could admit that Dr. Hauthal had proved any direct connection between the extinct ground sloth and the men who had obviously used the cave at some time in the past. No one takes seriously today the romantic if implausible story of the domestication of Mylodon by man.

One of the fascinations of palaeontology, however, is the element of surprise. The slow, plodding ways of getting facts—laborious study, endless digging, endless comparison of bone with bone, endless recourse to the data of other sciences—have been, and will be again, broken through by the improbable, rising like a coelacanth through the sea of knowledge.

Carbon-14 dating of the dung of the Mylodon of the great Patagonian cavern, now known as Mylodon Cave, has proved that the creature existed at least until 10,500 years ago. The circumstances which prompted Rudolph Hauthal to assume that prehistoric man in Patagonia had domesticated and used for food this fascinating, tough-skinned beast have largely been discounted. The grasses which Hauthal had taken to be cut hay provided for the stabled *Gryptotherium* are, according to later scientists, merely grasses broken off from those growing in the front of the cave and scattered throughout by winds and the men and animals who used the cave. The wall of rock running diagonally across the inner part of the great cavern does not appear to have been made by man, but rather to have fallen from a vaulted section of the roof, perhaps as the result of an earthquake. True, Dr. Hauthal did find, in the three-foot thick layer of dung in the lowest level of

View of the Mylodon cave

the cave, two bone awls obviously made by man. These might have been left there by men who were Mylodon's contemporaries. They might also have fallen from the middle level in the course of excavation. Man has definitely been traced back nearly 9,000 years in a cave not more than 150 miles from Puerto Consuelo. Yet what seems a devastating blow at Hauthal's domestication theory is the fact that among the bones said to have been broken by man and split for the purpose of extracting marrow, were found the bones of a huge jaguar-like animal which would have been very difficult for prehistoric man to cultivate as a source of

Gryptotherium

fresh meat. It is more likely, say those in a position to know, that
the bones were broken by rocks falling from the vaulted roof and
by the tread of heavy animals walking over them.

Perhaps the most astonishing thing about the palaeontologists'
study of the Consuelo Cove Mylodon is what it has revealed about
the beast himself and the nature of the land in which he lived. A
careful examination and analysis of the Mylodon dung has shown,
from the nature of the plant pollen contained in it, that the giant
sloth did not sit on his huge haunches and claw the leaves of trees
into his millstone jaws. There were no trees in the vicinity of

Mylodon Cave when its namesake lived there. How do we know this? Although there were many kinds of pollen found in the ten- or eleven-century-old dung of Mylodon, there was not a trace of tree pollen which must have been there had there been any trees for the animal to eat.

Perhaps equally surprising is the suggestion contained in the analysis of the body waste of the giant sloth that he and his kind came to their extinction as a result of malnutrition, rather than having been butchered by man. It is known that a deficiency of certain minerals in the diet of grazing animals, notably copper and cobalt, causes anemia and loss of vitality. We now know that Mylodon lived in an extremely arid region and that prolonged aridity causes a loss of copper and cobalt in the available grasses and shrubs. In the dung of Mylodon there is present only an infin- itesimal quantity of copper and cobalt. It is possible that there is still not enough evidence to accept, as proved, the idea of My- lodon's death as a result of malnutrition, but if more evidence is needed it will either be supplied by palaeontologists or prove by its absence in the light of research that the theory was wrong.

To add zest to this remarkable story, one mystery still remains. If man did not have actual contact with a complete Mylodon, alive or dead, how did the heavy skin which first drew attention to the Puerto Consuelo cavern and which appears to have been removed from the body, become separated from the bones which once wore it? Did ancient man, as Hauthal and at least two of his colleagues suggest, skin the great beast with stone knives? Un- fortunately no one has recorded the exact condition of the entire skin when first found and no abrasions made by stone knives have been noticed among the ossicles which lined the skin. Hauthal indicates that the hide was folded when found, but there is no proof of this and the statement can never be verified. We can only speculate.

11.

Epilogue
NEW LIGHT ON ANCIENT DARKNESS

IT HAS BEEN SAID in the first chapter of this book that there exists a gap in our knowledge of the development of life from the early algae and other plant forms of several billion years ago and the early forms of animal life found in fossils of what we call Cambrian rocks 500 to 600 million years old.

Until 1965, palaeontologists were unable to shed any clear light on what happened during pre-Cambrian times—that is, the period from 600 million to two billion years ago.

In the summer of that year Andrew H. McNair, professor of geology at Dartmouth College, who had in the course of several years of prospecting in the North learned of the presence of a series of pre-Cambrian rocks in the Canadian Arctic, took his son and two Dartmouth geology students and headed north to see what he could find.

Victoria Island, which was the party's destination, is about twice the size of the state of Pennsylvania. Its center is about 1,200 miles from the North Pole and about 1,000 miles east of

Point Barrow, Alaska. It is inhabited by a few hundred nomadic Eskimos (that is, Eskimos without any permanently settled habitation) and the staff of three Hudson's Bay trading posts, augmented by a couple of missions, a Royal Canadian Mounted Police detachment, and several DEW Line stations. The interior of the island is largely bare rock, glacial drift, and, in summer, grassy uplands which support some animal population of caribou and musk oxen.

Dr. McNair's party reached Victoria in July, with the help of Canadian government survey planes. The unpredictable weather gave them a lot of trouble, and the difficulty of getting about in the interior, where feet were the only means of transportation, was enormous. In the Shaler Mountains, a series of uptilted rock layers stretching diagonally across the island from Minto Inlet to Glenelg Bay, McNair was encamped during the last week in July. On July 25 he noticed an interesting rock ledge in a flat hollow below the summit of the mountain ridge. He was on his way back to camp and, being cold and tired, almost made a note to have a look at the spot on the following day. Something told him that there was no time like the present. That something was right. He made his way to the ledge and immediately knew that he had made a very important discovery. The supper cooked at camp that night began to take on the aspect of a party.

Dr. McNair had known that the Shaler Mountains were a pre-Cambrian formation and must have realized that although they had once been worked over by a glacier advancing from the southeast, they had never in their history of hundreds of millions of years been completely subjected to great and distorting strains which would have altered the rocks themselves and destroyed any fossil remains within them. This was because they were the remains of a covering over the very oldest basic rock of the earth's crust, upon which they were deposited. This covering, in Victoria Island and a few other places in Canada, had never been worn away or buried under later formations. Here at Professor McNair's feet, embedded in thin plates of shale-like rock, were the unmistakable fossils of extinct brachiopods (fairly complex, many-celled creatures with shells), mingled with the casts and tracks of wormlike creatures and a number of distinct but unidentifiable shapes resembling the spines of sea urchins or the pointed tubes of primitive molluscs. McNair could, at the time, only guess at the true age of the rocks, but he knew that they were much older than the known Cambrian formations in which fossils of living organisms (metazoans) had been found before this. Certain intrusions (molten rocks which had forced their way into the formation) were at least 600 million years old. The ancient rocks themselves, since they were there for the intrusions to enter, must have been very much older.

It is hard to imagine what Dr. McNair's feelings must have been at the moment of his discovery in that high swale of the Shaler Mountains. He knew that he had made a start at closing the gap between the known fossils of the Cambrian period and that far distant epoch of the two-billion-year-old algae of the Lake Superior shore. Until a reasonably accurate dating, obtainable by recently devised means, of the Shaler Mountains' rocks, he could not tell exactly how far into the past he had pushed the existence of a fairly complex form of life. Certainly it would prove to be much farther back toward the time when the earth was unable to support animal life than anyone had believed possible. Who could now say that the discovery of transitional forms, of missing links between the simple, single cells (fossils of which cannot be found in even the oldest rocks) and such relatively complex creatures as the brachiopods—or still higher animals such as the worms and molluscs which also have been found in the Victoria Island rocks —was beyond the reach of the palaeontologist?

Dr. McNair's discovery in Victoria Island is a far cry from the giants of the Wyoming badlands, the cliffs of Lyme Regis, or the Mylodon Cave, but it may turn out to be the most important palaeontological advance of our generation. We are, because of it, a step nearer to being able to date within reasonable limits the beginning of animal life.

A Selected Bibliography

SUGGESTIONS FOR FURTHER READING

Chapter 1

Lauber, Patricia. *All About the Planet Earth*. New York: Randam House, 1962
Moore, Ruth. *The Earth We Live On*. New York: Alfred A. Knopf, 1956

Chapter 2

Bush, Helen. *Mary Anning's Treasures*. New York: McGraw-Hill Book Company, 1966
Matthews, William H. III. *Exploring the World of Fossils*. Chicago: Childrens Press, 1964

Chapter 3

Clymer, Eleanor. *Search for a Living Fossil*. New York: Holt, Rinehart and Winston, 1963
Fenton, Carroll and Mildred A. *In Prehistoric Seas*. Garden City, N. Y.: Doubleday & Company, 1963

Chapter 4

Andrews, Roy Chapman. *All About Dinosaurs*. New York: Random House, 1953
Colbert, Edwin H. *The Dinosaur Book*. New York: McGraw-Hill Book Company, 1951
Darling, Lois and Louis. *Before and After Dinosaurs*. New York: William Morrow and Company, 1959
Matthews, William H. III. *Wonders of the Dinosaur World*. New York: Dodd, Mead & Company, 1963

95

CHAPTER 5

Hiser, Iona S. *From Scales to Fancy Feathers*. Chicago: Rand McNally & Company, 1962

Hylander, Clarence J. *Feathers and Flight*. New York: Macmillan Company, 1965

CHAPTER 6

Epstein, Sam and Beryl. *Prehistoric Animals*. New York: Franklin Watts, 1956

Fenton, Carroll L. and Mildred A. *The Fossil Book: A Record of Prehistoric Life*. Garden City, N. Y.: Doubleday & Company, 1958

CHAPTER 7

Robinson, W. W. *Beasts of the Tar Pits*. Los Angeles: Ward Ritchie Press, 1961

Stock, Chester. *Rancho La Brea: A Record of Pleistocene Life in California*. Los Angeles County Museum, 1958

White, Anne Terry. *Prehistoric America*. New York: Random House, 1951

CHAPTER 8

Colbert, Edwin H. *Millions of Years Ago: Prehistoric Life in North America*. New York: Thomas Y. Crowell Company, 1959

Robinson, W. W. *Ancient Animals of America*. Los Angeles: Ward Ritchie Press

CHAPTER 9

Clymer, Eleanor. *The Case of the Missing Link*. New York: Basic Books, 1962

Crump, James and Irving. *Dragon Bones in the Yellow Earth*. New York: Dodd, Mead & Company, 1963

Edel, May. *The Story of Our Ancestors*. Boston: Little, Brown and Company, 1955

CHAPTER 10

Andrews, Roy Chapman. *All About Strange Beasts of the Past*. New York: Random House, 1956

Rhodes, Frank H. T., Herbert S. Zim, and Paul R. Shaffer. *Fossils: A Guide to Prehistoric Life*. Wayne, N. J.: Golden Press, 1962

CHAPTER 11

Fox, William and Samuel Welles. *From Bones to Bodies: A Story of Paleontology*. New York: Henry Z. Walck, 1959

Index

THE AUTHOR

RAYMOND HOLDEN is a native New Yorker with a great variety of interests. In addition to writing and reviewing books, he is a director of Early Sites Foundation, a New England organization devoted to archaeological research, maintains a bird-banding station, and finds time to relax in his workshop doing carpentry work and mounting natural history specimens which he collects.

Mr. Holden's writing is marked by variety also—poetry, novels, mystery stories, biography. His adult titles include THE MERRIMACK in the "Rivers of America" series and THE REMINDING SALT, a book of his own poetry. For young readers he has written SECRETS IN THE DUST, the story of archaeology, FAMOUS SCIENTIFIC EXPEDITIONS, and other volumes. FAMOUS FOSSIL FINDS is his fifth juvenile book.

A graduate of Princeton, Raymond Holden lives with his wife, Barbara, in Newport, New Hampshire.

THE ARTIST

JOHN MARTINEZ, whose illustrations and jackets have enhanced a number of books in the juvenile field recently, received his training at the School of Industrial Arts, the Art Students League, and the School of Visual Arts. He spent three years in Mexico painting and studying, and his work includes murals, portraits, and technical and science fiction illustrating. He lives with his wife and young daughter in Richmond Hills, Long Island.